CELEBRITIES!
CELEBRITIES!

Mr. D's AMAZING ENCOUNTERS WITH FAMOUS PEOPLE

BY

JOHN T. D'ALESSANDRO

AN EXETER BOOK

Lornbroke Press, Inc.
Saline, Michigan

FORWARD

I am happy to say that this is the third book of my "Mr.D. series. An earlier book, "They Toll for Thee, Mr. D." published in 1995, surprised me greatly by being bought widely and read in many countries. I have received positive responses from Great Britain, New Zealand, and other English speaking countries. The book is now quite rare and has become a collector's item at high value.

My second book, "Teacher! Teacher! Mr.D.'s Amazing Adventures at Collwood High", loosely based on my experiences at Collingswood High School, in Collingswood, New Jersey, has been a very good seller on Amazon.Com. The book tells of how I crossed paths over the years with several celebrities, and I gather that is one of the reasons why many readers purchased the book.

Consequently, I have decided in this book, to devote all the stories to my "amazing" encounters with many famous people, from President Franklin Delano Roosevelt to Donald Trump. In all cases, I did meet these people, and they all impressed me very much.

Reading of my encounters, I hope will bring you enlightenment and enjoyment. You comments are quite welcome and you can contact me at the addresses below.

E-mail:
John T. D'Alessandro
jayteacher@bellsouth.net

Mail Address:
John T. D'Alessandro
Arts Condominium
1324 Locust Street
Apartment 307
Philadelphia PA. 19107

DEDICATION

TO MY PARENTS:

My wonderful mother:
        Teresa Totarella D'Alessandro
And to my loving father:
        Michael Anthony D'Alessandro
They were the most important celebrities
in my life!

JOHN T. D'ALESSANDRO

The author invites you to re-live with him all the wonderful encounters he had with famous people over several decades. He grew up in Collingswood, New Jersey, and graduated from Collingswood High School in 1947. He received a Bachelor of Science in 1951 from Temple University. After serving in the U. S. Air Force for 4 years during the Korean War, he returned to Temple University and received an M.Ed. He taught at three high schools prior to his 22 years stint at Collingswood High School, where he built a fine reputation as director of several school musicals and adviser to the school newspaper. He took a two year sabbatical in1971-72 to pursue doctoral studies at Oxford University in England. In 1990, he published his first book on "They Toll for Thee, Mr. D.", which was widely sold and read in the U.S. and abroad. After leaving public school teaching in 1982, he taught at colleges in the Philadelphia area. He retired to Florida for fifteen years in 1995. In 2011, he moved back north and embarked on writing this third auto-biographical novel. He currently lives in center city, Philadelphia, Pennsylvania, and enjoys all the cultural activities offered by a large and wonderful metropolis.

IN READING THIS BOOK YOU WILL JOIN WITH THE AUTHOR AND REMINISCE WITH HIM AS HE CROSSES PATHS WITH ALL SORTS OF WELL KNOWN PEOPLE: YOU WILL LEARN FACINATING AND UNKOWN FACTS ABOUT INTRIGUING PERSONALITIES, AND ENJOY STORIES ABOUT THEIR INTERSTING LIVES.

ACKNOWELEDGEMENTS

BOOK EDITORS: Ric BenSafed & Bill Clossey

Very Special Thanks to My Health Care Surrogates:
Bill Wilson, Ric BenSafed, Ray Giordano & Herb Boettger

Special Thanks for their help, concern and encouragement:
Susan F. McGarrigle, Rita McGarrigle, Michael D'Alessandro,
Andrew D'Alessandro, Bill Dietrich, Angela Dietrich, Diana La
Pergola, T. Patrick Hurley, Tad & Peggy Dynakowski, Jerry Bello,

**Thanks to my friends in Florida for their interest, concern and
support**: Eric Gillen, Robert Stevenson, Craig Goodman, Nancy
Mellon, Pam Armento, Susan Bailey, Steve & Linda Yaroch,
Winston and Merri Churchill

**Thanks to my friends in foreign countries for their interest,
concern and support**: Roel and Jolien Huisman (France), Tomasz
Andrazek (Australia) Paul Cunnningham (Dubai)

**Thanks to all my friends in the Philadelphia Area for their
interest, concern and support**: Ron Chucola, Frank Mosca, Judy
Podwil, Richard O'Malley, Bill Clossey, Ike Marconi, Howard
Silverman, Richard Sanders, Burt Gregory, Michael Gilbertson,
Roger Margolies, Carol Kaufman, Ellis Sacks, Fran Metzman, Bob
Alcorn, Mark Sandburg, Mina Smith-Segal, Laura Wilson,
John M. Smith, Steve Sacks, Thomas Charnock

TABLE OF CONTENTS: CHONICLE OF STORIES: "Celebrities! Celebrities! Mr. D's Amazing Encounters with Famous People"

(The date indicates the year when Mr. D. met the celebrity)

CELEBRITY 10. 1967   BRUCE WILLIS
                     Story:"Mr. D. He Ain't Fair!"

CELEBRITY 11. 1968   ROBERT F. KENNEDY
                     Story: "Mr. D. Meets Robert F. Kennedy"

CELEBRITY 12. 1969   STEPHEN SPEILBERG
                     Story: "The Greatest Nerd of Them All!"

CELEBRITY 13. 1971   THE GHOST OF OSCAR WILDE
       Story: "A Yank at Oxford" Oxford U. Fall Term 1972
       Story: "Matriculation Day, Oxford U., Fall Term 1972
       Story: "The Tutorial Session" Oxford U. Fall Term 1972
       Story: "Rag Week, Oxford" Oxford U. Spring Term 1973

CELEBRITY 14. 1972   J.R.R. TOLKEIN
                     Story: "They Very Manner of Things"

CELEBRITY 15. 1973   DEBBIE REYNOLDS
                     Story: "Mr. D. Meets Actress Debbie Reynolds"

CELEBRITY 16. 1976   QUEEN ELIZABETH
                     Story: "Mr. D. and the Queen of Great Britain"

CELEBRITY 17. 1977   WOODY ALLEN
                     Story: "Mr. D. Meets Woody Allen"

CELEBRITY 18. 1978   FRANK RIZZO
                     Story: "Mr. D. Meets Mayor Frank Rizzo"

CELEBRITY 19. 1986   DONALD TRUMP
                     Story: "Mr. D. Meets Donald Trump"

CELEBRITY 20. 1992   BILL GATES
                     Story: "Mr. D. Meets Bill Gates"

CELEBRITY 1: 1943: Franklin Delano Roosevelt (1882 – 1945)

At Harvard University: Age 19   **1938: Proposes "New Deal" Policies**

STORY:"The Kid and the President" Sept. 1943

No Fourth Term! No Fourth Term! No Fourth Term!" was the shouting from a group of college students. The great president, Franklin Delano Roosevelt, was about to speak at a rally on the steps of the City Hall in Camden, New Jersey, and some of the crowd was very hostile.

John D'Alessandro, who was later known as the author, Mr. D., was then a 9th grade student who had sneaked out of school to hear the great man. He was shocked to see FDR lifted out of a great open-topped limousine, put into a wheel chair, and rolled to the speaker's stand by the Secret Service. There, they stood him up and locked his leg braces, as the crowd demonstrated loudly, for and against, his election for a fourth term as President of the United States.

John was much annoyed by the disrespect of the college students, mostly from Rutgers-Camden University, who were all carrying protest signs. A tall, blond guy was carrying a sign saying, "12 years Is Enough! We Don't Need A Dictator!"

John responded: "We need this President! We can't change horses in the middle of the stream!"

"We heard that old saying before! Not even Washington served for more than 8 years! It's illegal!"

"Where in the Constitution does it say there is a limit for Presidents?"

"O.K but he tried to pack the Supreme Court to get his way!" said another collegian.

John was thankful that he had just studied the document at school. "Where does it say there is a number of justices to be on the Supreme Court?"

"Well, I don't care. Look at him. He's old and feeble!" said a third college man.

A heavy man with a foreign accent broke in. "At Yalta, this President gave away all of Eastern Europe to Stalin. Now my people in Poland are oppressed by the Russian troops!"

After some whirling, ear-busting sounds from the Public Address system, the great President began to speak in such a way that really thrilled John.

"There are 5 Freedoms all peoples must have. Freedom of Expression, Freedom of Religion, Freedom of Work, Freedom from Want, and Freedom from Fear," declared Roosevelt.

After some perfunctory applause, the Secret Service put FDR back into the wheel chair, rolled him to the open-topped limousine, and set him in the back seat. He gave forth his famous smile, puffed on a cigarette held in a cigarette holder, and held his arm out as he waved good-bye to the crowd.

John quickly ran up to the limousine, grabbed the President's sleeve and shouted, "Good luck, Mr. President. I hope you get your fourth term!'

"Well, young man, I certainly hope so; I certainly hope so!

Two Secret Service men grabbed him under his arms and pulled him back. The official caravan of cars quickly sped away, as John took a long, wonderful breath.

At the junior high school the next day, John was called to the vice-principal's office to explain why he had played hooky the previous day. The administrator did know whether or not to believe the story, so he gave the boy a month of after-school detentions. But John did not care. He had had a wonderful encounter with the most famous man in the world. He would always remember September 10th, 1943 as one of the best days of his whole life.

NOTE: FDR died 4 months after he was re-elected. Because of his fourth term, the 22nd Amendment was added to the Constitution which limits Presidents to two terms, but didn't apply to his successor, H.S.Truman.

Franklin Delano Roosevelt (continued)

Camden City Hall, Camden, New Jersey

On November 11, 1943, this was the site where President Franklin Delano Roosevelt delivered his famous *Five Freedoms Speech,* outlining the privileges that all people throughout the World should have. On that day, Mr. D., as a freshman in high school, approached the great leader and wished him good luck on his election to a fourth term. The great man led the nation through the Great Depression, World War II, and post-war conferences He had held the office for over twelve years when he died in 1945.

Franklin Delano Roosevelt (continued)

Yalta Conference (Crimea, U.S.S.R.)

President Roosevelt attended this conference, held from February 9-11, 1945 with Winston Churchill, Prime Minister of the United Kingdom, and Joseph Stalin, Premier of the Soviet Union to discuss Europe's post-war reorganization. Roosevelt mostly wanted Stalin to enter the U.S.S.R into the war with Japan. Yalta was the third of the three wartime conferences, preceded by Tehran, Iran, in 1943 and Potsdam, Germany in July, 1945. At this conference, Roosevelt was sickly and near the end of his life. Many historians think he made a bad deal with Stalin giving Russia control of half of Europe. Stalin agreed to free elections in the affected countries, but instead he imposed Communist governments and control by Russian troops. To the great resentment of the Polish people, the Russians did not leave Poland until 1999.

CELEBRITY 2:   1947: Joan Fontaine
(1917 – 2013)

1938: Hollywood Ingenue   1938: Major Hollywood Star

STORY: "Mr. D. Meets the Black Cat"

In Mr. D.'s tenth year of directing plays at Collingswood High, in Collingswood, N.J, he often reflected on his days working as a 19 year old stage apprentice in summer stock theater. He recalled that it was the summer of 1947, at the seaside theater at the tip of southern New Jersey, called the Cape May Playhouse. Like most of summer stock, the playhouse presented a new play every week and this week it was "Bell, Book and Candle" which later became the TV show "Bewitched." The famous actress, Joan Fontaine, was brought in to play the starring role. The movie magazines said she had "the most beautiful face in Hollywood"; it was a wonderful white, beautifully shaped face, and always had a hidden smile. Her main competition for most beautiful in Hollywood was her equally famous sister, Olivia de Havilland. Ms. Fontaine arrived in the Cape May with her secretary, hairdresser, dresser, and chauffeur and soon let everyone know that she, the grand lady of the theater, was in town.

Mr. D., whom everyone at the playhouse called "Johnny," was spending the summer mostly working on sets, putting them up, painting them, and then taking them down. Often the director would bellow out, "Johnny do this, or Johnny do that," and he was kept running constantly.

One of the characters in "Bell, Book and Candle" was a black cat named Thisepa, which in this play was a witch. The great actress was given a stuffed cat as a prop, but she did not like that at all.

"I have done this play before and we always use a live, tame cat. Get me a cat," demanded the prima donna.

"Johnny, find a black cat, dope it up with catnip, and make sure it is docile," said the director to the hapless, young apprentice.

Johnny searched and searched the neighborhood for a black cat. Finally, he found one feasting itself in a trash can. He spent his own money on high grade, canned cat food and doped the creature with lots of catnip. As he held it, it seemed as tame as could be, and it purred and purred in his arms.

On the opening night of the play, the famed actress was about to go on to the stage.

"Johnny, hand her the cat, dammit... right now!" whispered the director.

"Kid, is this cat tame? Is he doped up?"

"Yes, Ms. Fontaine... He's really lovable."

All went well for the first ten minutes of the play, but then the cat suddenly went wild, reached up and with his clawed paw, scratched "the most beautiful face in Hollywood!" There were four long, bleeding scratches!

"This Goddamn cat... that kid told me he was tame!" she shouted and threw the cat into the audience. The playgoers were in shock... but the great lady wiped the blood off her face with the back of her hand, gained her composure, and went right on with the play, but in a rather shaken and upset manner.

As the curtain came down, the distressed actress stomped off the stage shouting. "Where is that Goddamn kid, Johnny, or whatever his name. I'm going to kill him... I am going to wring his neck!! GET ME A PLASTIC SURGEON. I'M DISFIGURED FOR LIFE!!"

A real plastic surgeon was quickly brought in from Atlantic City, mostly to calm down the great star. Fortunately, the scratches were superficial and with some good makeup, were soon no longer noticeable.

The play went on for another six performances without incident, although Ms. Fontaine hated using a stuffed cat as a prop. Johnny hid mostly in corners around backstage, trying to avoid any possible wrath of the great lady.

After the last performance, it was the custom for the cast to go to the Wooden Jug Tavern down in Cape May village for a little celebration. That night Johnny was there, at the far end of the bar, drinking sasparilla. Suddenly, the doors of the saloon swung open wide and Fontaine and her entourage entered. Hardly anyone noticed her and this was too much for the "Grand Lady of the Theater." She was not to be ignored! She spotted Johnny at the far end of the bar and with grand gesture; she raised her arm and pointed. "There's Johnny, that wonderful, little stagehand! We've been searching for you all night. Where have you been, darling?" she shouted in the loudest, possible voice, with great sarcasm, to draw the attention of everyone there.

As she advanced on him, Johnny was shocked and shaking in fear. Had she come to kill him...? Or what?

"Bartender, a bottle of your best champagne and two glasses, if you please." The cork of the bottle popped.

"Well, here's your champagne and two glasses, but the kid can't drink. He's not of age."

"Well, if he can't drink it.. he can drown in it!" she said with a fierce tone of revenge as she poured the expensive wine all over Johnny's head. "And bartender, tell this little snot that he shouldn't hand a wild and vicious animal on stage to a star of the films. And make him pay for this lousy champagne!" she said taking a large drink.

After much forced laughter and loud talking, Joan Fontaine walked out of the bar with her entourage and had her chauffeur take them back to New York City that night.

Jackie, who grew up to be the respected high school teacher, Mr. D, was then stunned by this episode and quaked at the thought of it for years afterwards. But he wondered back then as a stage apprentice in 1947, "Was this what 'theater' was all about?"

Joan Fontaine (continued)

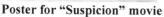

Poster for "Suspicion" movie   Poster for "Rebecca" movie

Mr. D. met Joan Fontaine when he was an apprentice at the Cape May Playhouse in Cape May, New Jersey, in 1947. The actress made forty-five major motion pictures and won the Academy Award twice, for "Suspicion" with Cary Grant, and for "Rebecca" with Lawrence Olivier. Both of these films were made by the great film director, Alfred Hitchcock.

Joan Fontaine (continued)

"The Constant Nymph" 1943: In this scene Charles Boyer, Peter Lorre' and Alexis Smith appear with Miss Fontaine

"Jane Eyre" 1944: In this adaptation of Charlotte Bronte's gothic romance, Miss Fontaine appears with Orson Wells

CELEBRITY 3: 1947: Albert Einstein
(1879 – 1955)

1902-09: Swiss patent office

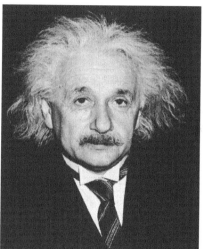

1921: Nobel Prize in Physics

STORY: "75 Cents for The Genius"

"Who has a quarter? We should stop at that little store and get some Cokes. They probably have a cooler," said Tommy Cromwell.

"Give me your quarter. I have a quarter. And Dick give me your quarter. And I'll go in this old store. Boy, am I hot and thirsty" said John, who was over heated and sweaty.

The three former classmates at Collingswood High had been joy riding around the Princeton, New Jersey, area on a hot summer afternoon. Tommy was in his second year at Princeton and his old buddies had come up to see him.

John could hear the screen door slap behind him as he entered the ancient, rickety establishment. He could smell the pungent odor of tobacco, various stale canned goods, and the chocolate candies. At the counter was an old, very portly lady wearing a multi-colored frock with her hair tied in a bun. While John went to the cooler and got three bottles of Coke, an ancient old man with wily gray hair tottered in the door. Although it was warm, he was wearing a well worn coat, over a baggy sweater.

"I want some chocolate covered mints. Would you please cash this check for me?"

"No way. I don't know you!" said the buxom lady in quite a huff.

John was aghast as he recognized the old man. "Lady, this is Albert Einstein, the very famous physicist. Einstein. "

"Because he is Jewish, you want me to give him money!" she said sharply.

"Lady, Dr. Einstein is one of most famous persons in the world. If you don't know who he is, you gotta be the dumbest person in the world!"

"Alright, alright. I had enough guff from you college students. You get out of my store and take that old Jew with you."

"How much are the chocolate covered mints that he wants?"

"Seventy five cents, cash, for you, kid"

John picked up the confection, gave the three quarters to the old lady, and then gave the candy to old man and helped him out of the creeky, old screen door and down the few steps.

"What is you name, son?" said the old man.

"John.. John D'Alessandro"

"Well, thank you very much for the candy, John." and then he turned and began shuffling up the road and through a gate which said "Institute for Advanced Study, Princeton University"

As he returned to the car, John had to face his very thirsty buddies. "Where's the cokes, you bum. Where's our money?" said his friend, Dick.

"You wouldn't believe it. But I spent the quarters buying candy for a great genius"

"What in hell are you talking about? Who was this so-called genius?"

"Albert Einstein, he came in the store, didn't have any cash, so I bought him some chocolates."

"No Shit! Albert Einstein!" said Dick. "That's wonderful, but I still wish you would have gotten the cokes!!"

Albert Einstein (continued)

Albert and Elsa Einstein, 1933

Behind this great man was this great woman: Elsa Einstein, Albert's second wife, who traveled with him from Berlin to Princeton in 1933 and brought along her two daughters from a previous marriage to form the cohesive Einstein family unit. He became an American citizen in 1940.

Einstein bicycling around the town of Princeton, 1933-55

Albert Einstein (continued)

Institute for Advanced Study: Princeton University, Princeton New Jersey: Only the greatest scholars, like Einstein and J. Robert Oppenheimer, were invited thinkers in residence

Mr. D. met Albert Einstein in 1949 in a candy store somewhere above Princeton when the professor was a scholar working at the Institute for Advanced Study (here shown).

Near the beginning of his career, while still in Europe, Einstein thought that Newtonian mechanics was no longer enough to reconcile the laws of classical mechanics with laws of the electromagnetic field. This led to the development of his "General Theory of Relativity" in 1916. This revolutionized the whole study of physics. He won the Nobel Prize in Physics in 1921. Einstein died in 1955, in Princeton, N.J., at the age of 76.

CELEBRITY 4:   1956: Michael Landon
(1936 – 1991)

Eugene Orwitz, Collingswood High

Principal actor in "Bonanza"

STORY: "The Baddest Kid Ever"

"Oh, you're not going to let Eugene Orwitz in your play!" said Miss Benevento across the lunch table.

"Hm, well," said Mr. D. slowly taking a sip of his coffee.

"Look, John, you just don't know the trouble that kid can cause. He's a devious monster in a glamour boy's body," chimed in Miss Gordon, trying hard to swallow some of her sandwich.

"Well, I really don't know the kid that well. Can he be that bad?" questioned Mr. D., not yet convinced.

Overhearing the words "Orwitz" and "bad," Mr. Coursen walked up behind Mr. D.'s chair. "John, Oogy, that's what the kids call him, is not bad. He is the *baddest*. He has the indisputable record in this school for most infractions of the public order!" The gym teacher wiped his brow and continued, "He *will* ruin your play. And the worse thing is that you won't be able to do anything about it. He is the slickest bugger I have *ever* met."

"Well, he appeared at try-outs yesterday. He was as good as gold. He read well, and he certainly is very personable and good looking. Maybe he can act?"

"Oh, he can act!" retorted the gym teacher. "He's the best actor in this school. He cons everybody in this place, and he could talk his way out of the state prison."

"This is the third time I've had him in French I!" exclaimed Miss Benevento. "And I don't care about all his stories and excuses. I swear I am going to flunk him again."

"He won't be at your 3 o'clock rehearsals until 3:30. He's in detention every afternoon until then. The school secretary told me Oogy has the high school record for most after school detentions," said Miss Gordon with great consternation.

"Don't trust him with anything. Since he won the state track meet in javelin he thinks he is a Greek god," said Mr. Coursen.

The next afternoon at a meeting of the play cast, Mr. D. was leery about Oogy and could hear the warnings of his colleagues in his ears. The play was *Topper*, a comedy about an "angel" who did good things but caused funny situations. Predictably, Oogy did wonderfully well in the reading for the lead role, but Mr. D. was cautious. He would not let this boy lead him into a trap. He would not be a victim of this boy's ego!

Mr. D. had asked other teachers to help pick the cast for the play, but, since the Old Guard always avoided such boring tasks; two young female teachers were the only volunteer judges. Of course, they were charmed out of their panties by the beautiful, glistening eyes and the handsome smile of the wondrous Oogy!

"No," Mr. D. said to the volunteer judges, "the other teachers say that Oogy is terrible to deal with. Putting on a play is hard enough without putting up with an uncontrollable prima donna. But I have to make some decision."

The next afternoon after school, Mr. D. strolled to the front of the auditorium. "Now students, I've distributed the rules and regulations for the play. The first two are the most important. First, be at rehearsals and be on time. Second, be completely cooperative. That means if you don't want to be serious and are here just to mess around, don't join this cast!"

A long, loud yawn was heard from among the group of students seated in the front rows of the auditorium. It was Oogy, taking an attention-getting stretch to indicate his boredom.

"Eugene Orwitz, I would like to talk to you after this meeting," said Mr. D. with a warning voice.

Oogy's facial display was that of a wounded deer. "Me? Oohh Mr. D., I swear I wasn't doing anything, just stretching a little."

Mr. D. smacked his lips and went on with the announcements. "Now, students, the cast list will be posted on the bulletin board in the cafeteria tomorrow. You all did pretty well in these try-outs today. Thank you very much for coming."

As the group slowly left the auditorium, Mr. D. approached Oogy, who was slouched deeply in a seat with his feet propped up on the next row.

"Put your feet down and sit up. Well, Oogy, how do you think you did in the try-outs today?"

"I was terrific," smiled Oogy. "I *am* an angel. The part was written for me!"

Mr. D. was surprised by the boy's audacity. "Well, we haven't picked the cast yet, Oogy. But if you should happen to get a part, I warn you, the first funny business, the first disruption..."

"Mr. D. ...Mr. D., why are you laying this on me now?" protested the boy with a great show of hurt.

"Well frankly, Oogy, you've got quite a reputation," replied Mr. D.

"Who said something? Those old foogies we've got around here?"

"O.K., you've got my warning. Now let's see what you do."

"Mr. D., I really respect you. You've got young ideas. I'd really like to prove to you that most of the things said about me are lies by people, who are jealous because I'm good looking and smart. I promise, on my bending knee, I'll do everything you say. Just give me the part."

Mr. D. was almost afraid that the boy would really get on his knees and beg. What teacher could refuse such contriteness, such humility? Mr. D. was in a quandary: He dare not give Oogy the lead, and yet he could not exclude him from the cast on hearsay. A compromise was the only solution; Oggi would get a very minor role, and, also, be assigned to take care of the lights from the backstage switchboard.

The play went into rehearsal and practices went well, except for the various distractions caused by Oogy. He would flip the house lights off and on and pretend that he was just "testing", or that it was a mistake, or that it was his honest ignorance. He was always joking, telling stories, amusing the girls, and making funny noises. He really could not endure *not* being the center of attention - the "life of the party." But the boy was careful to keep his transgressions small; none yet was serious enough to cause him to be fired by Mr. D.

On the Friday of the eighth week of rehearsal, Mr. D. tried to start Act II, but nothing was going right. The stage crew was uncooperative, the set was not getting done, and there was a malaise among cast members who mostly stayed in the rear hall out of the sight of Mr. D.'s controlling eyes.

Suddenly a senior girl of the cast came running from rear stage in a fluster, exclaiming, "Mr. D.! Oggy is messing around back there! And he's being fresh with the girls!"

"Oggy, please come out here!" shouted Mr. D. angrily over the P.A. system. No Oogy appeared. "Oogy!" shouted Mr. D. once again. The boy came out with the look of an angel on his face. "Oogy, this is it! This is all I'm taking! You're out! Now get out of the auditorium!"

The student departed in a cloud of disgust saying nothing but slamming down books, kicking seats, and stamping his feet as he furiously exited up the auditorium aisle to the rear doors.

In the ninth and last week of rehearsal, Mr. D. felt that everything was under control: The costumes were finished, the sets finally functioned, the lighting script was set, and even the dress rehearsal went well. Then disaster struck. Louis Asenfelter, the lead boy playing the "angel," got sick with laryngitis and could not utter a word. Mr. D. held a glum meeting with the cast and crew over what to do. Who could learn the part, 150 pages of script, on one day's notice? Who?

"Get Oogy. He could do it," uttered Mary Leaming, the student director.

"What?" screamed Mr. D. "Oogy was here, and I had to get rid of him because of his poor behavior. Are we going to eat humble pie?"

"Don't make any difference. Oogy is the only one around here who could do it. He has the moxie. We gotta have Oogy or there's no play," said the stage manager, Paul Wise, shaking his head.

Mr. D. took a long breath and then, after a long pause, relented. "All right, Mary, go find him."

On opening night of the play, fortunately or unfortunately, Oogy was amazing, playing the part with great swagger. He didn't know all the lines but he knew the story and ad libbed artfully. At the curtain calls, he took the standing ovation like the Emperor of Ethiopia! He acted as if he had won an Academy Award and, needless to say, the teachers of the Old Guard were annoyed. Some hated his audacity and believed he didn't deserve such honors; others just felt it would make him so much more the worse.

As the school year went on, there were "Oogy" stories from staff members almost every day. Oogy had punched a teacher; Oggi was excluded from the Senior Trip; Oogy had won the state championship in the javelin, and on and on. The notorious student was "last in his class," but tied for the "honor" with a retarded girl. Oogi was not to receive his high school diploma until he made up 315 hours of detention!

About July 15th after that school year was over, Mr. D. went to the high school office to check his mail. The heat was sweltering and he hated to interrupt his vacation. There was Oogy seated on the detention bench in front of the school office. He had been there every day from 8:00 in the morning until 3:00 in the afternoon since school had closed making up his periods of detention!

"Stick around, Mr. D.," said Mr. Olinger, the vice principal, "at 12:00 we're going to give Oogy his diploma, finally!" At the appointed hour, there was not much of a graduation ceremony. Mr. Olinger simply called out with a diploma in hand, "Eugene Orwitz." Like a rising storm, the boy grabbed the document, let forth a hurricane of obscenities, and stormed out the door, not to be heard of again until years later.

Ogy's great ability with the javelin got him into college in California and from there it was only a short expedition to the studios of Hollywood. After a job or two as an extra, and appearing in some B movies, by sheer moxie he was cast in *I Was a Teenage Werewolf.* Subsequently, he got a role on a long-running Western show, *Bonanza,* playing one of three brothers. This role led to another long running series, *Little House on the Prairie,* and later to many other projects.

All America grew to love the famous "Michael Landon", the stage name taken by Eugene Orwitz. Although Michael Landon became the wealthiest actor in Hollywood, Mr. D. never watched any of his TV shows. He could too well remember when the "angel" in his school play gave him the misery of being "the baddest kid ever!"

Michael Landon (continued)

Collingswood High School, Collingswood, New Jersey

Mr. D. directed Eugene Orwitz, later known as the famous Michael Landon, in the play, "Death Takes A Holiday" when he was a student at Collingswood High School, NJ, in 1956-57. He was very clever and personable, but because he was an unruly pupil and unwilling to do school work, he got very poor grades and tied for the last place in his graduating class. He was on the football team and was a star athlete on the track team, being picked as the Scholastic High School Javelin Champion of the U.S.

Michael Landon (continued)

"Bonanza" western TV series ran from 1959-73. Lorne Greene played the father of the Cartwright family with sons Pernell Roberts, Dan Blocker, and Michael Landon as "Little Joe"

Scene:" Bonanza": Dan Blocker, Pernell Roberts, and Michael Landon

CELEBRIY 5:   1960: Eleanor Roosevelt
(1884 – 1962)

1949: UN delegate   **1960: US Ambassador to the UN**

STORY: "Mr. D. and the First Lady of the World"

As Mr. D. rushed into the faculty meeting, late as usual, Principal Crawford Lance of Collingswood High was speaking sternly.

"As you all know, we will be greatly honored at the end of this month by a visit from Mrs. Eleanor Roosevelt, the wife of the great President, Franklin Delano Roosevelt. This is happening due to the good graces of Mr. Palmer, who was formerly the custodian of the Hyde Park residence of the Roosevelt family in New York. Mr. Palmer worked there 20 years with the National Park Service. Mr. Palmer is also the father of one of our students, William Palmer and has arranged this wonderful event"

"For this very special occasion we will bring into our Irvine Gymnasium all students of the Collingswood schools plus the schools of all the sending districts. We will be asking all boys to wear suits or sport coats and ties and the girls to wear their best dresses. Yes, Mrs. Bear?"

"This may not be very popular with the students or their parents."

"Mrs. Roosevelt has been called the First Lady of the World. She is our United States Ambassador to the United Nations. We have to show the press of the world that this is not some hick high school in some hick town. Yes, Mr. D?"

"Who will be introducing Mrs. Roosevelt?"

"Our governor of New Jersey, Robert P Meyner, has promised to be here and do the introduction. We will be setting up a large platform towards the back of the gymnasium. I have asked our vice principal, Mr. Ridinger, to meet the governor and escort him to his place on the dais. I am also asking Coach Hughes to meet the mayor and the town council and escort them to the dais. The students will take their seats in the gym at 1:00 and they must remain absolutely silent before and after Mrs. Roosevelt speaks. She will begin her address at 2:00 and I understand she will speak for about 45 minutes. And I am asking all teachers to be on the gymnasium floor that day to ensure the good behavior of all the students."

As the rather glum Mr. D. left the library, Principal Lance stopped him. "Mr. D., since you are the expert on proper behavior and decorum -"

"I am?"

"I am asking you to meet the ambassador's limousine. She will have her English aide with her. You should escort them to the office of the women's coaches in case they want to freshen up. Then show them to the speaker's platform."

"Yes, certainly, Principal Lance."

Four weeks later, the big day arrived. About 2,500 students were marched into the gymnasium under the watchful eyes of their teachers. Mr. D. heard the sirens of the state police cars as the governor of New Jersey arrived. Then in a flurry of honking horns, the diplomatic car from the United Nations arrived at the curb in front of the gym, and Mr. D. rushed to open the door for Mrs. Roosevelt and her aide.

"I'm Mr. D., Madame Ambassador; I am to be your escort into the hall. First, we will stop at the office of the women's coaches, just inside the building...in case you want to freshen up before your speech."

"That's quite kind of you, Mr. D. Please lead the way."

For a change, that office and bathroom had been all cleaned up and were made quite immaculate that morning.

"Which way is the loo?" questioned the ambassador's officious aide with a most proper British accent.

"Here, I'll open the door." Mr. D. tugged on the door, but it was locked. "Oh, I am so awfully sorry. One of the women coaches must be in there." Dread filled Mr. D.'s heart. How could this happen?

"This is absolutely intolerable, you dumb clod! You're a sorry escort," scolded the aide. The English teacher began to sweat.

"No, No, Mr. D. I'm just a common person like everyone else. I will wait my turn... How many pupils do you have in your high school and what percentage are minorities?"

"1200 and we have no black students. This is an all white town." Mrs. Roosevelt was visibly annoyed, as she was a known civil rights advocate. "I wish Mr. Palmer had told me that before he invited me here. Well then, tell me about your family."

Mr. D. went into a long discourse about his mother and father, his three sisters and his twin brother, all to take up time. Then Mrs. Roosevelt decided to talk about her five sons and what they were now doing. After a long while, Mr. Ridinger, the vice principal rushed in.

"Mr. D. please, please bring the ambassador and her secretary into the gymnasium. We have a huge audience waiting and waiting."

Mr. D., much distressed, whispered in the vice principal's ear that the restroom there was locked.

"Mrs. Roosevelt, I am very sorry about this problem. Please come with me next door to the male coaches' office. It may be a little dirty, but there is also a lavatory there. There's is no one in this rest room. Obviously, the cleaning lady inadvertently locked the door from the inside. Mr. D. you can go to the auditorium. I will take care of this," said Mr. Ridinger

Almost 3,000 adults and pupils loudly applauded as Mrs. Roosevelt finally entered and stepped up to the podium. She spoke for almost an hour about the need for world peace and said that only the United Nations could bring that about. Her remarks were followed by polite applause.

All the teachers and administrators, the mayor and the council, everybody, were so relieved when the ambassador's car departed with the screaming sirens of the state police. Mr. D. was still shaking from his great mistake. For all his intelligence, he could not get the First Lady of the World into a bathroom. He wondered why all these calamitous things always happened to him at Collingswood High. He was very upset and tense.

After it was all over, the downhearted teacher was approached by his principal. "John, I never thought you would let us down. I am very disappointed. That English lady, the Ambassador's assistant, really tore into me. She said you were an unthinking bumpkin."

Mr. D. made no response. As he walked home that day, he weakly sang the school song to console himself, "Blue and gold forever...Colls color bright. To you we're loyal and we will fight with all our might. Blue and gold forever ever will fly. Collingswood High School. Cheer her to the sky."

Eleanor Roosevelt was the First Lady of the country during the thirteen years her husband was President of the United States. After his death in 1945 she served as the US Ambassador to the United Nations for six years. Mr. D. met Mrs. Roosevelt when she visited and spoke at an student assembly at Collingswood High School in Collingswood, New Jersey in 1960

Eleanor Roosevelt (continued)

1943: Mrs. Eleanor Roosevelt with Mary McLeod Bethune, president of Bethune-Cookman College, in Daytona Beach, Florida

As first lady, she was a great promoter of African-American rights and was passionately committed to the ideals of social justice. She viewed racial discrimination as an evil which had been tolerated for too long in the United States. She actively cultivated relationships with civil rights leaders, such as Dr. Mary McLeod Bethune, and was at the center of civil rights history, including the desegregation of Washington D.C. She knew as First Lady that she had the ear of her husband, the President, and used that access to promote the cause of voting rights for black citizens of the country. She was fiercely opposed by Southern conservatives in the South.

CELEBRITY 6: 1961: Johnny Carson
(1925 – 2005)

1961: "You Bet Your Wife"
TV show from NBC, NYC

Host, "The Tonight Show"
for thirty years

STORY: "Mr. D. Plays Hooky"

In his 2nd year as an English teacher at Collingswood High School, in Collingswood, New Jersey, Mr. D. got a call from his old Air Force buddy. His friend, Rodger Bronner, wanted Mr. D. to meet him and his wife at the Taft Hotel in New York City the very next day.

"Cough! Cough! Cough! Mr. D coughed heavily into the telephone as he dialed the high school. "Is this Vicki Hancock, the school secretary?" Hearing an affirmative response, he went on. "Well, this is Mr. D. Cough! Cough! Cough! Cough! I am terribly sick, Vicki. I just can't come into school tomorrow. Can you get me a substitute?" The lie worked, and he was off to the big city the next day.

After a great reunion lunch, the three visitors to the big city were walking down 5th Avenue when a page from Radio
City Studios approached them and offered them tickets to the
Johnny Carson Show, called "You Bet Your Wife". It was a great program taped in the afternoon, with Carson and his side kick, Arthur Treacher joking and cutting up.

Then came the point in the show where the comic wanted a participant from the audience. Mr. D. slumped in his seat and pulled his winter coat over his head. Carson spotted the errant teacher. "Get that guy with the coat over his head!" Mr. D. would not move.

"Ushers escort that man to the stage."
After being dragged to the stage, Mr. D. identified himself as a teacher. Carson asked what he was doing in New York City. "I'm here with an old Air Force buddy, and he and his wife and I are seeing the town."

"Well, Arthur," said Carson, "I've heard of students playing hooky, but a teacher? Well, audience, what do you think about that?"
The audience gave forth with a huge scolding "ooh!" to the delight of millions of T.V. watchers of NBC. The show was seen throughout the United States at 4:00 that afternoon.

"Well, you and your friends have a good time in New York, and we won't tell a soul that you were here!"

The audience gave forth a roar of laughter.

When Mr. D. got back to Collingswood High School on Monday, it seemed that everyone there and in the whole town of Collingswood knew about the hooky-playing teacher. So many had seen the broadcast. At the high school there were whispering that Mr. D. had been on the Johnny Carson Show on Friday during school time, but no one would mention it to him. Mr. D. tried to avoid running into the principal, but when he did, Mr. Lance, with a gleam in his eye, just slyly commented to him. "I heard you had a very bad cold last weekend."

Johnny Carson (continued)

Johnny Carson, the star of the "Tonight" show often interviewed famous persons. Sometimes he used wild baby animals for laughs.

Johnny Carson (continued)

Ed McMann, Carson's sidekick, questions "The Great Karnac", in a comedic role, about the funny messages

Carson jokes with Ronald Regan, who became U.S. President

CELEBRITY 7:   1962: Richard Nixon
(1913 – 1994)

1932: Football star, Whittier College   **1952: Elected Vice President**

STORY: "Mr. D.'s Boys Terrorize Nixon"

"Now settle down!! Please get quiet!"

Crawford Lance, principal of Collingswood High School, was trying to get an assembly of 200 seniors in the school's auditorium to pay attention to him.

"We called this assembly today to make sure all seniors who are going on the Senior Trip to Washington, know the rules exactly: 1. There will be no alcohol whatsoever on this trip 2. At the hotel in Washington no boys will ever be in the girls' bedrooms. 3. There will be absolutely no messing around. If there is any trouble whatsoever, I am telling you, this will be the last Senior Class that ever goes on a Senior Trip. Mr. D. and some other teachers will be chaperones for the boys. Miss Mellinger and some lady teachers will be the chaperones for the girls. We will be getting on the train at the Collingswood station at 6:00 on Tuesday. You can bring fruit and other snacks. Yes, Brittany?"

"Can we bring oranges, Mr. Lance?"

"Yes, but you must not make a mess."

As the students filed out of the auditorium, Mr. D. was approached by Tom Steely. "I'm glad we are going. It should be great!"

"Well, Tom, will the boys be good boys or will I have trouble?"

"Mr. D., you know we're always good boys," he responded mischievously.

On Tuesday morning around 5:30 the parents started to drop off their kids at the station, and at 8:00 the Pennsylvania Railroad train pulled out for the nation's capital. It was a rather calm ride, just a lot of buzzing, but Mr. D. noticed that all the students were sucking on oranges.

The senior trip covered all the usual sites in the Capital. On his evening rounds of the corridors of the Winston Hotel, which had balconies all around an atrium, Mr. D. heard some boys giggling in one of the girls' rooms, but he decided to let it go. On the third day, the students were dog tired and ready to go home. Mr. D. went into a double room that housed eight boys, mostly football players. Only a very heavy, red faced boy remained there.

"Herbie, where are the boys?"

The boy stammered and tried not to answer. "Herbie, you tell me what they are doing, or you are going to be in a lot of trouble!"

'They've filled up bags of water. They're going to drop them off the fourth floor of the atrium down to the lobby floor."

Just then Mr. D. heard loud noises, like gun shots. He ran to the balcony outside the door and could see and hear great commotion: sirens, police whistles, some screaming, and great turmoil, all down on the lobby floor. Secret Service agents were all over the place. They ran up to the 4th floor to the bedroom of the Collingswood boys with guns drawn.

A Secret Service agent grabbed Mr. D. and ushered him into the bedroom. There were seven very humbled boys in handcuffs.

"I'm Mr. D. from Collingswood High School. I'm their chaperone."

"There has been a very serious breach of national security!"

" Now, agents, these are just high school boys playing a prank. Take off the hand cuffs, for God's sake!"

"Now, wise guys, when you dropped those water bombs down into the lobby, did you know Nixon was entering the building?" the agent asked.

"Skippy DeMarco whispered, "Who's Nixon?"

"The Vice President!" whispered his pal, Steve Mangano.

"The vice president of what?"

"Of the United States, you dumb ass!"

"Mr. D., doesn't your school teach about our government?" said the agent.

"I'm an English teacher. Don't blame me," Mr. D. responded lamely.

"The Vice President is very upset. An attack on the Vice President means 25 years in federal prison."

"Twenty-five years! Jesu, we won't see any girls until we're 50 years old. You guys made me do it!" screamed Skippy waving his arms.

"Oh, shut up and sit down!" ordered his team mate.

"Agents, interrogate these culprits, so we can make a report to Mr. Nixon. Mr. D you come with me" The senior agent escorted the bewildered teacher to a suite on the second floor and into a large room. There, sitting by the window, was the Vice President himself.

"Mr. Nixon, this is the teacher who was with those kids. They call him, Mr. D."

"Well, Jesus Christ, Mr. D., when those kids dropped those water bombs on me from the fourth floor of the atrium, did they know it was me?"

The teacher gulped a bit. "Honestly, Mr. Nixon, I don't think so."

"God damn it, Murphy!" speaking to his aide "with Eisenhower as President, I must be the most obscure Vice President in the history of the country. And that s.o.b. hasn't called me this month. He could at least invite me to a Cabinet meeting. You know, Mr. D., Alvin Barkley, Vice President under Roosevelt said the Vice Presidency wasn't worth a warm bucket of spit. And more and more at this God damn job, I believe it!"

"Well, sir, you're still the presiding officer of the U.S. Senate, " said the aide.

"Oh, fuck the Senate. I sit up there on the dais like a wooden Indian and listen to their pompous bullshit, and I can't even vote. Fuck that. I never go there. All I do now is go to horrendous funerals of two-bit dictators. The last one was the President of Tajikstan. I stood at that cemetery in the Ural Mountains for four hours and froze my ass off!

Changing the subject and looking straight at Mr. D. he questioned, "So you say it was all a prank. Well, it was a damn good prank. I used to pull pranks all the time at high school and college. You know I played football for Whittier College, and the coach was a real sonna ma bitch. Somebody put glue in his hat. I'm not saying who did it, but, boy, did I laugh my ass off!"

"Alright, Brightman," speaking the Secret Service agent, "you can let the little bastards and their teacher go... And Mr. D., an election is coming and you better vote for me."

"Ah... Ah... I can't do that. I'm a Democrat."

"What? Now I change my mind. Keep this freaking left-leaning liberal under arrest!"

Mr. D. was about to faint and his face turned pure white.

"Oh, come on, teacher... Ha! Ha! I was only kidding. But you better damn well keep this whole incident a top secret. I can just see the headline in the Washington Post: "High Schoolers Terrorize Nixon!" If this story leaks, I assure you it will mean federal prison. Now you take those little bastards back to where in hell you came from and forget you ever saw me!"

Back at the boy's room, Agent Brightman gave the verdict to Mr. D. "We are going to escort these boys to the train station. You are never to come to Washington again. Also, you must never reveal what happened here today... Or, I warn you, there will be grave consequences!"

On the following Monday after the trip, Collingswood High School and its students were humming along as usual. Tom Steely, the editor of the school newspaper, approached Mr. D. laughing. "You never found out! Hah! Hah! Hah! I'll tell you a secret, if you promise to God that you will never tell the Principal or the faculty. All those oranges that the kids were eating on the train were spiked with vodka. Britney Smith's father is a doctor and she got the syringes, and the girls did it."

"Well, I have a secret too. But I'll never tell, even under torture."

Suddenly, Principal Lance approached. "Mr. D. I want to compliment you and the other chaperones on running a perfect senior trip. No alcohol, no girls and boys getting together, and no bad incident. Just great! I think we can start planning for a senior trip for the Class of '63 next year."

Mr. D. just shook his head and thought, "Are all principals so dumb?"

Richard Nixon (continued)

Richard Nixon was Vice President under President Dwight Eisenhower from 1953 to 1961. Mr. D. met him at Westin Hotel in Washington D.C. in 1962.

Richard M. Nixon was elected as 37th President in January 1969, and reelected in November, 1972

Richard Nixon (continued)

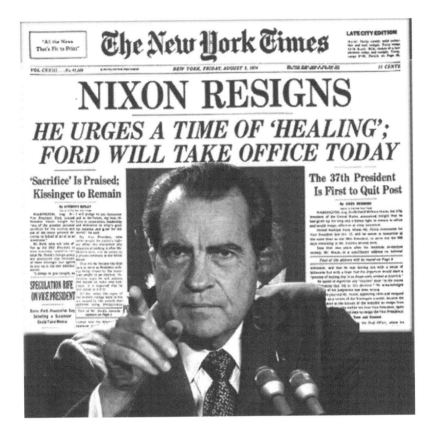

In 1973, a Washington scandal began as Nixon's operatives broke into the headquarters of the Democratic Party. After that scandal and all sorts of "dirty tricks" were revealed, he lost much political support. He was impeached by the House of Representatives, but resigned on August 9, 1974 before the case could be decided by the Senate. He was granted a pardon, by his successor, President Gerald Ford. He suffered a debilitating stroke in April 1994 and died at the age of 81 at his seaside home in California.

CELEBRITY 8: 1964: Martin Luther King
(1929 – 1968)

1955: Harvard Ph.D. degree   **1964: Nobel Prize Winner**

STORY: "Mr. D. Supports Martin Luther King"

"In the name of justice and equality, this institution, Campbell Sr. High School, is hereby closed forever," pronounced Dr. Martin Luther King, the famous leader of the Black Civil Rights Movement. "As Thomas Jefferson said, 'we hereby declare that all men are created equal'. There is no reason why poor black children have to attend this dilapidated building with broken windows."

This happened in "Black Town", the poorest section of Daytona Beach, Florida, in 1964."

Assembled before the old high school with Dr. King were his black acolytes, various other leaders of the movement including Whitney Young, A. Philip Randolph, and James Farmer Jr., and a motley group of 200 black and white activists, protesters from various civil rights group, nuns, preachers, and a sprinkling of human rights promoters from several states. Also, in the audience was John D'Alessandro, a teacher, from New Jersey with his two retired teacher friends, Paul Miller and Tom Blancett. These friends lived in Daytona Beach and had heard about the "peace march", and Mr. D., as their guest, just couldn't miss out on meeting this famous celebrity.

Dr. King looked out on the audience and began to question in a sonorous tone. SSir, you with the blond hair. Would you object to using a drinking fountain just used by a black lady?"

"Absolutely not, Dr. King"

"And you with the red hair", pointing to Mr. D. "How do you feel about using a toilet just used by a black man?"

"It wouldn't bother me, Dr. King."

"Why are you here, you're not a brother?"

"It's like Jefferson and you said, 'All men are created equal', and the color of one's skin can not change that! And I am a 'brother'."

The whole entourage left Black Town, and marched with an American flag across the Main Street Bridge, singing "We Shall Overcome!" led by singers from a wonderful church choir. They were followed slowly by about 20 patrol cars, with roof lights spinning, from the Volusia County Sheriff's Department.

When the group arrived at small oceanside park, there were lavatories labeled: "White Men Only," "White Women Only," "Black Men Only," and "Black Women Only". Also there were drinking fountains labeled: "Whites Only" and "Blacks Only"

Dr. King walked right up to them and shouted: "These hateful signs must come down, and now!" His black acolytes were there with crow bars and pick hammers ready to do the job, but they hesitated in much fear. Everyone could see the line of Sheriff's deputies in the rear led by Sheriff "Duke" Johnson, a huge man wearing a white police hat with gold scramblings on the visor. The deputies all had their bully clubs out and were tapping the palms of their hands with their wooden sticks. The activists there knew that destroying county property was a criminal offense, and they could be attacked at any moment.

"Shall we do it, Dr. King?" said James Framer Jr. in a trembling voice.

"These signs of hate must come down. Do it now!"

There was tremendous tension in the air, as the protesters and sheriff's men shuffled about. . The situation was so electric that everyone there felt that a great catastrophe was about to happen.

"These deputies are going to arrest us all, I bet!" whispered Mr. D.'s friend, Paul, in a shrill voice.

"They're coming with those clubs. They are going to beat the shit out of all of us!" said Tom, Mr. D.'s other friend.

The black acolytes began ripping down all the wooden signs.

Mr. D. thought, "What 'n hell am I doing here?" He felt a yellow streak coming right down his back and he wanted to run. He didn't want his head bashed in.

Minutes upon minutes went by. What was going to happen?

Suddenly, Whitney Young, a very brave activist, rose up the pole with the American flag, and the preacher's wife, Coretta King, began singing the National Anthem: "O say can you see by the dawn's early light. What so proudly we hailed at the twilight's last gleaming?......"

The sheriff's men, sworn to uphold the Constitution, stood at attention and were totally embarrassed into being patriotic. They had no choice; they had to sing or seem unpatriotic. And as unwilling as he was, Sheriff "Duke" Johnson, gritting his teeth and huffing away, began mouthing the words of the anthem.

As the last lines were sung: "Oh, say does that Star - Spangled Banner yet wave. O'er the land of the free and the home of the brave?" the sheriff deputies started heading back to their patrol cars, led by a baffled Sheriff "Duke" Johnson. And as all there, black and white, sang at their loudest, the dangerous situation was diffused.

That day in the summer of 1964 all the wooden signs of discrimination in Daytona Beach were torn down, and no one every thought again about replacing them.

Mr. D. had had an experience of a lifetime. Although he still admits, to this day, that at that time, he was scared "shitless"; he felt good that he had risked "his butt" for Dr. Martin Luther King and the cause of Civil Rights.

Martin Luther King (continued)

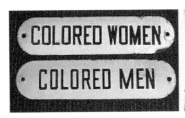 

JIM CROW SIGNS

Dr. King led civil rights protests in cities all around the South. In every march he tried to get the Jim Crow signs taken down. Mr. D. was with King's group when they took down the signs of discrimination in Daytona Beach, Florida in August of 1964.

Martin Luther King (continued)

In October 1960, Martin Luther King Jr. was sentenced to jail in Atlanta for leading a civil rights demonstration. Robert F. Kennedy interceded with a judge on his behalf and had him released. The preacher led marches in many cities to have Jim Crow signs removed.

Mr. D. met the preacher in 1964 during a civil rights protest in Daytona Beach, Florida.

Martin Luther King (continued)

STORY: "In The Spirit of Martin Luther King!" Collingswood High School, Feb.,'66

Of all the extra duties assigned to Mr. D. as a teacher at Collingswood High School, the only task that he really liked was directing the annual high school musical. The enthusiastic director had picked the Broadway musical, "West Side Story". Although it was a beautiful adaptation of Shakespeare's "Romeo and Juliet", Mr. D. had to convince the principal, and then the School Board, that it did not glorify gang warfare and teenage promiscuity. It was a musical drama to promote tolerance among different peoples.

In 1967, Collingswood was a lily white town and had been so since the American Revolution. It was a white land of snobbery and prejudice ruled by conservative Protestants. Mr. D. often felt annoyed by its sub-surface bigotry. He had never taught a minority student in the all-white school, until Jocelyn Jones arrived for try-outs for the play.

The production number, "The Dance at the Gym," called for couples to do three choreographed numbers. Jocelyn was really a better dancer than many of the white girls, and Mr. D. could not deny her a part.
All was going well at rehearsals, until the principal, Mr. Lance, looked into the auditorium and spotted Jocelyn Jones on the stage dancing with a white boy, Harry Smith, the captain of the football team.

"Who is that black girl?" whispered the old man with alarm.

"Jocelyn Jones, a new girl. Isn't she a terrific dancer?"

"Has she been absent from any rehearsals?"
"Well, just a couple of times," explained Mr. D.
With a "you know what I mean look" Principal Lance said,

"If she is absent again, drop her from the cast. We can't have that!"
Mr. D. told the girl to be sure not to miss any rehearsals. The devil was upon him. Here was his chance to "desegregate" this lily white school to the distress of the principal, the school board, and most of the townspeople.
Mr. D. weighed the risk. Earlier that year he had asked the principal for new vocabulary books. The principal said he would think about it. He had hoped that the principal would give him a new teaching contract with a $50 raise in it. The principal said he would think about it. Most of all he hoped he would be considered for tenure.

The challenge was upon him. Mr. D. could be like Rosa Parks who got on that public bus in 1963. Like the four black men who sat at the counter of the Woolworth Store in Birmingham in 1964. the spirit of Martin Luther King was upon him. Whatever the risk, he would let the black girl, Jocelyn Jones, dance with a white boy in the school musical! After all, it was 1966, and he was willing to take the consequences.

The production went on, right up to the full dress rehearsal. As the cast lined up to go on stage, "Mr. D. screamed at the student company manager, "Where is Jocelyn? " Mr. D. was in a panic, "Where is she?" There was a substitute dancer available, but what about his grand plan to show the world that Collingswood was not a narrow, hateful, bigoted town.

Linda Marsh, the student director, came forth. "I think Jocelyn has dropped out of school." Mr.D. gasped in pain and disbelief. He was ready to sacrifice his reputation, the whole production, his job.. And she had dropped out of school.

After the first performance, Principal Lance came up to him, looking quite pleased, and said, "I'm glad you did the right thing, dropping that black girl, Mr. D."

Mr. D. did get his new vocabulary books, his $50 raise, and his tenure, but he felt he had sold his soul for it.

"West Side Story" was written to teach tolerance of minorities, but the real message was lost. Jocelyn Jones, a real minority, was not up on the stage. A real teaching moment was lost. Mr.D. had blown his great moment of satisfaction and glory. Integration of Collingswood High was not to be had at this time in 1966.

CELEBRITY 9:   1966: Michael Landon
(1936 – 1991)

1956:US Javelin Champion **1974-82: "The Little House on the Prairie" TV program**

STORY: "First Amendment Blues"

The *Colls High News,* the school newspaper, was thirty years old when Mr. D. took over as adviser back in 1958, during his first year as a teacher at his Alma Mater. It was a challenge improving the school paper that he had worked on as a student. Under his tutelage for several years, the four-page, biweekly paper went on to win several awards from the various school press associations.

Although subscriptions reached over 1,000 during his sixth year as advisor, Mr. D. endured trouble and complaints with every issue, and he looked desperately to out of this troublesome responsibility.

After the publication of each issue, there was always discontent. Parents complained when a child's name had been omitted from the Honor Roll listing, the football coach or team did not like the coverage of the last game, the tennis coach felt that his team was not getting enough coverage, the facts about the last dance were all wrong...The biggest blowup occurred in 1964, and it concerned Collingswood's own movie star, Michael Landon.

Landon, whose real name was Eugene Orwitz, was remembered at the school for his constant disregard for every school rule ever invented. He was probably a pretty smart fellow, but his spunky insolence caused him unending trouble and constant failures in most courses, including three times in French. He was probably the school's most ardent underachiever, and Mr. D. had his own private memories about the arrogant student he had coached in a play in 1959, during Mr. D.'s second year at Collingswood High.

When the famous Michael Landon visited the high school in 1966 to chat with Bert, the janitor and some of his old teachers, he suddenly arrived at Room 203, sauntered in, and closed the door behind him.

"Well.. Mr. D.. are you still given out detentions?'

"Hello, Oogy, yes, to any student that deserves it."

"Well, I guess I deserved all those detentions. I certainly raised hell around here. Remember when I almost drove you crazy giving the Junior Play?

"Yes, I remember. Oogy. Well then I read that you doing very good in Hollywood. How is it?

"Making a Western on the back lot of Warner Brothers Studio isn't much fun, but it pays a lot of money."

"By the way, I know Coach Diemer has asked you if the school could establish an award in your name. You know, you ARE the most famous person to graduate from this school."

"No way.. I'm no good example. No student should try to be like me. They should set up a Mr. D. Award instead."

"Why? What outstanding thing did I ever do?"

"Well, you put up with bad asses like me, And you did help me get into San Diego Junior College even though I was last in my class."

"Oogy, all I ever did was to send your transcript to several colleges. San Diego Junior College accepted you because you were the National High School Javelin Champion."

There was banging on the classroom door.

"Damn it, those girls are looking for me. I got to run. Great seeing you Mr. D."

In the street alongside the school were the screaming members of the whole student body waiting for the television star. Landon hated the fuss and feared being hurt by the unruliness of the crowd, so he quickly jumped into a passing bread truck and escaped.

The *Colls High News* reported that Landon still held the school's all-time record for the number of detentions given to student. It also reported that he had graduated last in his graduating class, that he was made to sit on the school office's hard bench until the middle of July, making up 315 hours of detention before he could graduate!

Because Michael Landon was making millions in Hollywood, the Collingswood Board of Education regarded him as their most successful graduate (in monetary terms) from the high school. The *Collwood High News* report of the celebrity infuriated school board members, and they ordered all copies carrying the story "to be recalled, confiscated and destroyed!" How could the school paper "demean" this famous "son"? An immediate retraction was demanded and ordered of Mr. D.!

Mr. D. was greatly upset by the turn of events. What about the First Amendment? Freedom of the press? Journalistic integrity? Had students no rights of free speech?

He wanted to stand by his student editors, who had the story accurately, so he put in a call to the superintendent of schools,

Dr. James Mason, usually reasonable administrator said, "John John!, the Board of Education is furious on this one. Now don't put your job on the line. Get back as many of those papers as you can, destroy them, and then come out with a new edition with a retraction."

To make matters worse, the school's old principal, Mr. Lance, forced Mr. D. to go on the school's public address system with an embarrassing announcement. "The Superintendent of Schools has ordered that all copies of the November 13th edition of the *Colls High News* be returned to the high school office."

The students quickly caught on, and not only were few of the November 13th copies returned, but the copies of the "forbidden edition" soon became collectors' items.

Subsequently, Mr. D. had his student editors check the story. All facts were correct, *but* Landon had *tied* for the last place in his graduating class with a retarded girl. The last item had to be the retraction if an admission of inaccuracy had to be made.

In the next edition of the *Colls High News*, there appeared a simple statement: "In the news story concerning Michael Landon, the editors of this newspaper incorrectly reported that the Hollywood personality had graduated last in his graduating class. The editors regret this error."

The storm blew over, but Mr. D., was determined to get off this hot seat. A cautious conversation with Mr. Lance, the principal, was in order.

"Mr. Lance, I wanted to tell you that I would prefer not to act as adviser for the school paper next year. The school musical is very demanding, and I would like to put all my energy into that."

"Well John, I'm really sorry to hear that, but I can't relieve you unless we can find a replacement. Do you know anyone who would take your job?"

"No," said Mr. D., knowing that everyone on the teaching staff would rather work in the salt mines than take up the time-consuming job as journalism adviser!

"Well," said Mr. Lance, "you're just going to have to hang in there for another year to give us some time to find somebody else for your job."

Certainly not satisfied, Mr. D. now felt entirely doomed and said, "But, Mr. Lance..."

"Now look, John, you keep putting out those editions! And watch out what those kids put in them. Meanwhile, I'll see what I can do about getting you those literature books that you've been nagging me about."

A bargain had been made! A sneaky one at that, by an old codger who knew how to horse trade when necessary. Mr. D. needed the literature books desperately, and old Mr. Lance was not averse to making a crafty deal once in a while!

"Dear God," thought the exasperated Mr. D. as the principal hurried away, "now what will I have to do to get new curtains for the stage in the auditorium?"

Michael Landon (continued)

From 1974 to 1982, Michael Landon wrote, directed, and starred in a hit TV program *The Little House on the Prairie*, making him the highest paid actor in Hollywood (scene from the show). He passed away in 1991 at the age of 54.

An American western drama series starring Michael Landon, Melissa Gilberts and Lindsay & Sidney Greenbush & a large cast of characters

CELEBRITY 10: 1967: Bruce Willis
(1955 – present)

1967: at Pennsgrove H.S.   **1988: Began "Die Hard"
                                       movies**

STORY: "Mr. D., He Ain't Fair"

"Whites have rights! Whites have rights! Whites have rights!"
Mr. D. had been bought into Pennsgrove High School to help a former student and English teacher at the school, Jana Gillespie, to direct the school's musical. He was eating his lunch in the teachers' lunch room with her when he could hear the chanting outside.

"What going on out there?" questioned Mr. D.

"There's a lunchtime protest out in front of the school. They're protesting discrimination against whites, and it's all about you!" said Jana.

"What the hell? How did that happen?"

"You and I cast Will Williamson as the lead in the school play. Bruce what's-his-name, the president of the student council, has called the kids out of class in protest? He's out there giving speeches."

"That little bastard. He must be angry because he lost the lead role in the school musical to a black kid," said Mr. D.

Thump! Thump! Thump! To the thumping of a beating drum, the chanting of the protesting students went on.

"Mr. D., he ain't fair! Mr. D., he ain't fair! Mr., he ain't fair!"

"This has gone too far! The principal should stop this!" demanded the harried teacher.

"Mr. Wiley is not going to do anything. He won't get involved when it comes to a matter of race," said Jana.

As Mr. D. and Miss Gillespie left the lunch room and were racing down the hall to their classrooms, they were stopped by Mr. Wiley, the school principal

"Mr. D., I hear you and Jana cast a black boy in the lead role of the school musical. What's going on?"

"I admit it was my idea, but Will Williamson is terrific. He can really sing and dance."

"What about the rest of the cast?"

"Well, it looks like all the white kids are boycotting the show. They were just out there protesting in the courtyard."

"Look Mr. D. This school is dedicated to integration. We are not going to have an all black school musical."

"Well, on Broadway they are doing an all black "Hello Dolly" starring Pearl Bailey and Cab Calloway. It's great."

"Well, this high school is not Broadway. If I intervene, the NAACP is going to be right on my back. You caused this problem. Now you fix it!" ordered the principal.

"Jack, what are you going to do?" questioned Jana.

"We can't drop Will Williamson as the lead. The black kids will revolt. We have got to get the white kids, and especially that Bruce kid, back in the play,"

"Jana, I've got to get to the root of the problem… that cocky little egotist is causing all the trouble. I need to speak to him privately. You send him a note saying that he should see me after school in the auditorium."

At the end of that school day, the surly boy appeared in the cavernous Pennsgrove High auditorium.

"Mr. D. you wanted to see me? Look, I'm busy, I've got to go to baseball practice."

"Hold on. What's your beef, Bruce?"

"Everyone knows you and Miss Gillespie favor these black kids. We've had enough! The black kids have taken over the basketball team, the football team, the cheerleaders... And we're not going to let them take over the school musical!"

"Well, I don't think this is really about the black or white kids. I think this is all about you"

"Ya? Well, I think that guy who wrote "The Music Man," Meredith Wilson, never intended the lead to be a black guy."

"Will Williamson may be black, but he can really sing and dance...maybe better than you can."

"I was great in the junior play last year! Wasn't I? You're taking away my big chance. I want to be an actor. I want to be on the stage. My father wants me to stay here in Pennsgrove and work in his hardware store. He says with my lousy grades, he wouldn't pay for me to go to college. I hate hardware... in fact I don't like Pennsgrove very much, either."

"Come on Bruce, can't you be reasonable? You can have the second lead, the part of Marcellus."

"Me? Playing second fiddle to a black kid? Anyway, why should I do anything for you? I'm failing Senior English. I might not even graduate."

"Look, if you take a part in the play, you can get extra credit in English. You can pass English and you can graduate."

"That's nifty... Then what do I do? Sell nails and screws at my pop's hardware store."

"Yes, work at your father's store, save some money, then take off for New York and to the Broadway theatre."

"New York, the Broadway theatre? Yah... but don't I have to go to college or drama school first?"

"No, not really, if you're good looking and talented. What you should do is take some singing and dancing lessons... That's all you need. If you are ever going to get in a show in New York, it will be a musical. Take it from me, from my experience. Directors do not care about academic background. If they like you, they will hire you. Besides, almost all resumes presented by actors to directors have a lot of false stuff."

"So, I can lie about my background? That's good. Hmmm... Let me think. O.K., so will you help me get out of this hick town?"

"Yes, I will do what I can. I will even fix you up a resume', and we can plan on your going to New York City."

"Really, no shit? Mr. D.?"

"Now report here for play rehearsal this afternoon, and bring the rest of the white kids with you."

After all the fuss, Mr. D. was pleased with the production of "The Music Man." Will Williamson was a great "Music Man," and Bruce was hilarious as "Marcellus." All the races and the NAACP were pleased. Bruce Willis graduated and went on with his life... and to New York City.

Mr. D. didn't coach any more musicals at Pennsgrove High, but two years later he heard through the grapevine that Bruce Willis had gotten into the chorus of the Broadway musical "Grease" at a very young age.

About 10 years later, Mr. D. was driving down the main street of Pennsgrove, New Jersey, and he stopped by chance at the Willis Hardware Store. In the window there was a statuette from the Emmy Awards, which are honors for the best work in television. On it was engraved: "Bruce Willis, Best Actor in the TV Comedy series, 'Moonlighting.'"
Looking at the prestigious award, Mr. D. just shook his head and said to himself, "I guess I gave Bruce the right advice. He is on his way to stardom now!"

Poster for The Musical   Final Number: " The Music Man"

Mr. D. directed Bruce Willis in "The Music Man" at Pennsgrove High School in 1966. Willis had wanted to play the lead role, but agreed to play the secondary lead of "Marcellus" if the teacher would help him go into theatre and to New York City.

Bruce Willis (continued)

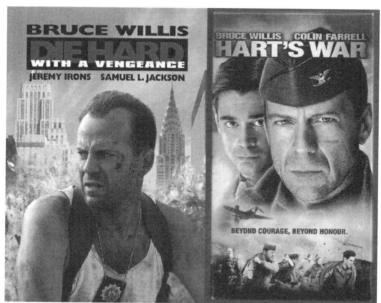

Poster: "Die Hard"   Poster: "Hart's War"

Bruce **Willis** in scene from "Die Hard" with Samuel L. Jackson

CELEBRITY 11: 1968: Robert F. Kennedy (1925 – 1968)

1960: Political advisor   **1968: Presidential candidate**

STORY: "Mr. D. Meets Robert F. Kennedy"

"A couple of hours ago on television, President Johnson announced that he not running for re-election. He looked old and haggard and he said he felt the American people no longer supported him." This was the comment from Dave Cosky, Mr. D's fellow teacher at Collingswood High and another war protestor.. They had arranged to meet in Mitten Hall at Temple University, in Philadelphia, as both were undertaking graduate courses there.

"Well, President Johnson is right. He has sent 500,000 troops to Viet Nam, 40,000 killed, thousands wounded, and we still can't beat the Viet Namese people," said Mr. D.

"Well, also, Robert F. Kennedy, quickly announced his candidacy for the presidency"

"That's great. Bobby has said he opposes the continuation of the war. He has enough star power that as President he could stop that senseless conflict!" hoped Mr. D.

"Also, it also came over the radio; Bobby will speak to the students here in Mitten Hall next Thursday afternoon, April 9. You're here on Thursday afternoon for classes aren't you?" asked Dave.

"Well, I would come anyway. Bobby is my big hope that the killing of my former students will stop.. just stop."

Mr.D. was practically traumatized with the death of each former pupil in the terrible war. He often spoke to his English classes in sad remembrance of them, and he would let no one sit in their former seats in his classroom:

2nd Seat First Row
Chris Cowen, Class of 1965, a mischievous con artist, a real likable kid with a face of freckles and jet black hair. Died in Saigon

4th Seat 4th Row
Robert Marshall, Class of 1965, tall, quiet, good looking, much in love with his high school sweetheart.. Married before he left. Died in Cam Rah Bay. Never saw his one month old baby.

5th Seat, 6th Row
Steve Smith, Class of 1962, a chubby, friendly lad with a crew cut. Likable. Terrible handwriting
Lt. U.S. Army. Died in the Tet Offensive

3rd Seat, Middle Row
Denny Leary, Class of 1967, one of the most popular members of the class. Joined military with classmate John Hill. Denny died in his arms during a fierce battle. He was only 19 years of age.

Mitten Hall at Temple University was built like a medieval castle with a large court yard in its center. Mr. D. and his buddy, Dave, arrived early in the great chamber April 9th to be close to the speaker of the afternoon, Robert F. Kennedy. Known as "Bobby", he was especially hopeful of getting the support of young people, especially college students. He was greeted by the student body with great whistling and applause. The Secret Service escorted him to the speaker's stand. His speech largely promoted great social programs, really an extension of Johnson's "Great Society"

When asked where would all the money come from, he sharply answered "From you! When you start paying taxes!"

In forceful words he announced his credo. "I believe that any who seeks high office this year must go before all Americans, not just those who agree with them, but also those who disagree, recognizing that it is not just our supporters, not those who vote for us, but all Americans who we must lead in the difficult years ahead."

Mr. D. spoke up, "Mr. Kennedy, what are you going to do about the Viet Nam war?

"Good question. What is your name, sir?"

"John D'Alessandro.." I'm a teacher in New Jersey, and a protestor against that horrific war. Four of my former students have been killed!"

"Well, young man, you tell your fellow teachers and all the protestors, that the day that I am inaugurated as President, the war will stop!"

After the speech, he came down from the stage, and shook hands with many in the crowd. When he approached Mr. D., he said in his most pronounced Boston accent, "I am very sorry to hear about your students. We shouldn't have more students die. We can't have that."

After that appearance, Robert F Kennedy went about the various states, winning many primaries, but he knew he had to win California in order to win the nomination. He did win California, and he addressed his supporters shortly after midnight on June 5, 1968 in the ballroom of the Ambassador Hotel in LosAngles. He was told that a short cut to the press room was through the hotel kitchen. There he was shot three times with a .22 caliber revolver by a 24 year old Palestinian, Sirhan Bisharea Sirhan.

After a very extensive funeral and days of national mourning, he was buried next to his brother, President John F. Kennedy in Arlington Cemetery, Virginia. Mr. D. vowed never to forget him.

Robert F. Kennedy (continued)

Robert F. Kennedy   John F. Kennedy

     Robert F. Kennedy was the campaign manager for his brother John F. Kennedy in the 1960 presidential election. They won the election defeating Richard M. Nixon by a narrow margin. He served in his brother's administration as Attorney General for 3 years, until the elder brother was assassinated.

     In 1968, immediately after he heard that President Johnson would not run for re-election, the younger Kennedy began his own campaign for President. Mr. D. met "Bobby" when he was speaking to students at Temple University in Philadelphia promoting his candidacy.

Robert F. Kennedy (continued)

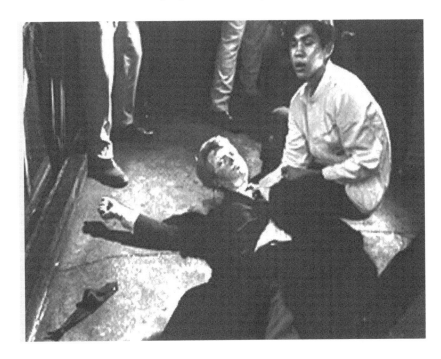

Assassination of Robert F. Kennedy, 1968

After winning the California and South Dakota primary elections for the Democratic nomination for President of the United States, Kennedy was fatally shot as he walked through the kitchen of the Ambassador Hotel, in Los Angles, California. He died in the Good Samaritan Hospital twenty-six hours later. His assassin was a 24 year old Palestinian/Jordanian immigrant, who was convicted of the murder and is serving a life sentence. After an extensive funeral, Kennedy's body was interred in Arlington Cemetery, next to his brother, President John F. Kennedy.

CELEBRITY 12: 1969: Steven Spielberg (1946 – present)

1969: Collingswood High   **Academy Award, 1993, "Schindler's List"**

STORY: "The Greatest Nerd of Them All!"

It appeared to Mr. D. that at almost every high school where he had worked, there was a group called "techies" or "nerds." At Collingswood High there was such a group, who were often playing "Dungeons and Dragons" in the cafeteria or chess after school.

Long ago, a wise teacher told Mr. D. that these students were always either very short, thin, small, or tall, never good looking but really brainy. They really didn't care for homely girls, but were crazy about the cheerleaders. But if a cheerleader gave even one of them a glance, the whole group would be happy all day.

Anyone could identify techies as they were usually pushing a cart with audio-visual equipment up and down the hallways. They suffered abuse in silence. "Why doesn't this projector work?" "That projector was supposed to be here 10 minutes ago!"

Another domain of the techies was the lights and sound equipment in the auditorium, and, in this respect, Mr. D. needed the cooperation of this group desperately. When Mr.D. decided that the school musical would be the Broadway musical, "Mame", the senior class invested a small fortune in royalties, scenery, and costumes.

The lead was Kathy McCarran, a talented senior. When she was given costumes previously worn by Angela Lansbury on Broadway and rented from a New York costume company, she immediately became a Prima Dona of the first order.

Taking the idea from Cecil B. De Mille, the great film maker, Mr. D. like to run rehearsals in the Collingswood High auditorium by standing on a 14 foot ladder placed in the orchestra pit.

Approaching Paul Weiss, the student stage manager, he asked, "Who do you have on the left follow spotlight?"

"Stevie, the ninth grader from Haddon Township."
"What's a ninth grader doing in the light booth?"

"He begged and begged me, so I thought I would give him a chance."
"Well, can he handle it?"

"He's really smart. He beats all the kids in "Dungeons and Dragons" and he is a whiz in chess."

Mr. D., on the P.A. system, shouted up to the light booth.
"Look, Stevie, or whatever your name is, when Kathy comes out for her big solo at the end of Act I, you'd better have that spotlight on her or she will be singing in the dark. Stevie, do you hear me? Do you understand?"

A weak voice was heard from the light booth at the top of the auditorium. "Yes, Mr. D. I will do it. I understand."

"If you screw up, Stevie, I am going to come up there and kick your butt. Do you understand?"

In the ensuing weeks, the cast, the orchestra, and all the backstage crews went through the rehearsals smoothly, and it all looked pretty good to Mr. D.

On opening night, Mr. D. was regaled in a dark tuxedo. His philosophy was that he had done all the training that he could, and now the show belonged to the students.

Alas, when Kathy McCarran, as "Mame", came out for her big song at the end of Act I, to Mr. D's horror, the spotlight was on the left side of the stage. The orchestra played and Kathy started to sing in the dark. She then darted to the left end of the stage. The spotlight moved quickly to the right where she had been. She darted back to the right, the spotlight moved to the left. Back and forth, back and forth, and on and on it went. The audience went into spasms of laughter. Finally the spotlight caught her in the center of the stage. Kathy then screamed, stamped her foot, and stormed off the stage in a rage to the great amusement of the audience. Then they applauded for about five minutes and the show could not go on. Fortunately, it was intermission.

From the back of the auditorium, Mr. D. could hear screaming and commotion in the hallway behind the stage. It was Kathy having a temper tantrum. "These techies are out to destroy me. I hate them! I hate them! I'll never go out on that stage again!"

Mr. D. appeared on the scene. "Now, Kathy, calm down. It was just an unfortunate mistake!"

"The hell it was! Those degenerates are out to destroy me. They hate me and I hate them. Get my understudy to finish the show!"

"Now look, Kathy, I will personally go up to the light booth and run the follow spotlight myself. I guarantee there will be no further trouble with the spotlights."

Somehow Kathy and the cast got through opening night in fine fashion, but Mr. D. wanted to immediately correct the situation.

"Paul, get that kid Stevie down here."

"He won't come down. He's crying...and he's afraid you will really kick him in the butt!"

When Stevie did appear, he was all choked up and tearful.

"Now Stevie, we all make mistakes. You tried your hardest. And I'll tell you what I am going to do. I am not even going to fire you. Tomorrow night you do the best you can with that 1500 watt spotlight."

As the last of the audience was leaving the auditorium on that opening night, two administrators approached Mr. D.

Also approaching was a tall man wearing a press badge and carrying a pencil and pad.

"Mr. D. this was really fine production. I'm Jim Shivers, drama critic for the Philadelphia Inquirer. I never cover high school plays, but my niece is in your chorus."

"Well, Jim, thank you for the compliment. This is our principal Mr. Lance, and Mr. Ande, our superintendent."

"Well, gentlemen, you have a really talented director here. But I can tell that that bit with the spotlight going back and forth was the funniest things I've ever seen. Who thought of that?"

Mr. D. hesitated, "Some student on the stage crew."

"Well, what's his name? I want to put it in my column."

"Stevie...Stephen Spielberg, from Haddon Township."
Mr. D. then yelled to the stage crew chief. "Get Stevie Spielberg down here, now!"

The school administrator had to get into the conversation with a comment.

"That young man, although only in ninth grade, is our school chess champion," said Principal Lance.

Stevie appeared with fear on his face as if he had done something terribly wrong, "You wanted me, Mr. D?"

"This man is Jim Shivers, from the Philadelphia Inquirer. He has asked to speak to you."

"Well, Stevie, so the funny bit with the follow spots was your idea? That was the funniest thing I ever saw on stage."

"Well, ah...." stammered Stevie.

"Well, what are you going do when you graduate?"

"I won't graduate from this school, my father and I are moving to Arizona at the end of the school year."

"Do you want to go to college, Stevie?"

"Yes, yes...After I finish high school in Arizona, I want to go to a film school, like the UCLA Film School. I want to make films, maybe I... maybe I can make some great films. I already have lots of ideas!"

"What ideas do you have, Stevie?" asked the reporter.

"One is about a man-eating shark; another is about a weird, little visitor from space."

The reporter, not wanting the boy to go on and on said, "Well, I am sure that your teacher here, and these administrators, and I, surely wish you a lot of good luck. You are a very clever young man. I am sure you will do well."

With that, Stevie Spielberg rushed away, back to his sanctuary in the light booth way up in the auditorium, far above all the excitement of the Broadway musical on the Collingswood High stage, to ponder on his ideas for great filmmaking.

Steven Spielberg (continued)

Movie poster for "Jaws"   Movie poster for "E.T."

Mr. D. taught Steven Spielberg as a student at Collingswood
High School in Collingswood, New Jersey in 1969. After his
attendance at the University of Southern California's film
school and several film apprenticeships, Spielberg was soon
directing his own films. He gained early success in Hollywood
with the motion pictures "Jaws" and "E.T." As of 2016, the
director has made twenty outstanding films including "Saving
Private Ryan," "Indiana Jones, Raiders of the Lost Ark" and
"Jurassic Park". He won the Academy Award in 1961 for
"Schindler's List"

Steven Spielberg (continued)

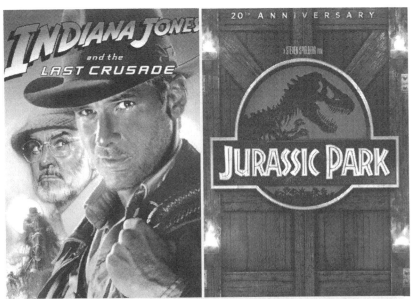

Movie poster: "Indiana Jones" Movie poster: "Jurassic Park"

"Indiana Jones and The Kingdom of The Crystal Skull"

CELEBRITY 13: 1971 The Ghost of Oscar Wilde
(1854 – 1900)

1878: Student, Oxford University   1895: Playwright: "The Importance of Being Earnest"

STORY: "A Yank at Oxford"

In 1971 Mr. D. was accepted as a Don at Oxford University and given permission to work on a doctorate. He knew he was entering the world of Oscar Wilde as it was said that the ghost of the writer still roamed the halls of the college buildings and was seen strolling about the University greens in the twilight of evenings. In preparation, Mr. D. had re-read Wilde's only novel, "The Picture of Dorian Gray" and the famous play, "Salome'". With the book of Wilde's epigrams in hand, he flew off to England and then traveled to the great medieval city.

The bells of Oxford were ringing in the distance as Mr. D. came out of the railroad station and caught a cab. He poked his head out of the window

of a taxi as it wound its way from the Oxford Station up to High Street. All about he could see the great, ancient buildings of the town. He relished the wonderful environment that was to be his home for the next two years!
At last, he had fulfilled a dream – to be a don at Oxford with full rights, privileges, and responsibilities. Ever since he had visited the University for a summer session in 1962, he had plotted and planned his study at the world's most famous university.

The old town was a bustle with streets filled with honking cars and sidewalks filled with pedestrians rushing about. He could see the proper, well-dressed townspeople going about the various shops, and he could see the students in their short scholar's gowns rushing from one college building to another.

The portal keeper came out of the great gate as the cab drove up to the huge, medieval, stone complex that was Merton College. Taking Mr. D.'s heavy bags, he led the new mentor into the first courtyard.

"Blaxton, the portal keeper, at your service, Suh," said the portly, ruddy-faced man. "From the colonies, eh, Suh?"

"Yes, from New Jersey. Ever hear of that place, Blaxton?"
"Er, I believe so, Suh. Near Callyforn-ia, isn't it?"

"Yes, near California, Blaxton," said Mr. D. not wanting to make a point of the man's ignorance. "This is fantastic here. How old is this place?" asked Mr. D.

"'Bout 1100 years, Suh. Merton was one of the first coalledges, you know, Suh. 'Ere comes Mr. Boon, your scout, Suh."

"Scout? What's a scout, Blaxton?"

"'E's sorta a body servant, a butler, you might say, Suh. 'E'll take good care of you, Suh."

A formally dressed old man with beautiful white hair came hobbling across the stones of the courtyard.

"He looks like a really old fella, Blaxton," observed the new don.

"Boon, Suh? Boon's about seventy-five, I guess, Suh. 'E's been here in service since 'e was a lad of fifteen."

With great decorum, the old man bowed and said, "Master John, Hannibal Boon at your service, Suh. Come right this way, and I'll get you settled in proper, Suh."

Mr. D. felt somewhat embarrassed to have the old man carry his "cases" but he knew better than to deny the old man his duty. "It will be apartment 6 C in Mob Quad, won't it, Mr. Boon? Warden Roberts promised in a letter that I would have those rooms for lodgings."

It was very important to Mr.D. as local legend at Oxford said that Oscar Wilde had lived in those very quarters.

"Yes Suh, Master John. Mob Quad – oldest University quad in the entire world," bragged Mr. Boon in a most dignified Cockney accent. "Right this way, Suh."

The second courtyard beyond was completely surrounded on four sides by a stone, residential building four stories high. An apartment, a "set," in Oxford terms, was a living room and a bedroom. Mr. D. soon found out that the "loo" was way off in the back area across the lawn. Each doorway on the quad had a stairway which led to six sets, with only one scholar to each set.

The trudge up the several flights of stairs was a strain to old Mr. Boon, but though he was breathing very hard, he tried not to show it. A large wooden outer door led to a walnut door and thence to a nicely furnished living room. "'Ere 'tis, Suh," gasped Mr. Boon putting down the bags and going to open the windows. "Most folks would not want this set. Right under the chapel bells, you know. Most folks couldn't stand that, Suh."

"I especially requested this set, Boon. I will love hearing the great bells of Merton Chapel. Whenever they do ring."

"Well, they do ring and ring, Suh, every hour, night and day. But I guess there's great history to these digs, Suh. That's Sir Isaac Newton's desk there, they say. Wrote some of his great mathematical theories right on that wood, Suh." Then pointing to the built-in window seat he continued, "And right there, at the window, Keats, that poet fellow, wrote his 'Ode to the West Wind,' Suh."

Looking out the window, Mr. D. questioned, "Who are those people going into that doorway over there, Boon?"

"Tourists, Suh, going into the Merton College Library. Oldest college library in the English-speaking world. They even got books in there by old Geoffrey Chaucer, hisself, Suh. And you know, right upstairs in this attic, old Professor Halley with 'is telescope discovered the Halley's Comet. Yes, Suh, right up there, Suh."

They went through a small door into a small bedroom with plain white walls. There was a small sink, an even smaller mirror, and an electric water heater mounted on the wall. "How do you get this thing to work, Mister Boon?"

"Just snap this switch, Suh. Takes 'bout fifteen minutes for some 'ot water, Suh. And see this bed, Suh. Oscar Wilde's it was, Sur, 'Bout the greatest student we ever did 'ave 'ere at Oxford. Ever 'ear of 'im, Suh?"

"Well, certainly, Boon. After all, I am an English teacher."

"Old Oscar, 'e took a double 'first,' ya know. T'over the Sheldonian Amptheater, he give the Salutarian speech at 'is graduation, and then 'e runs across the hall and gives the Valedictory speech. Folks still telling stories 'bout 'im till this day, you know, Suh. Well, Suh, I'm 'ere for every little thing ya wants, Suh. To take care of your dirty laundry and your cleaning and errands and such."

"Well, I will be much obliged for your kind help and advice, Boon."

"And you might buy your akeydemic gown right off, Suh. Clerkwells on the Haymarket is the good shop. Reasonable. You'll be needing it for the Matriculation Ceremony on Thursday. And if I do say so, Suh, get a heavy one. Drafty and cold 'bout some of these old halls at Oxford, you know. And you'll need a mortar board hat too, Suh."

"Yes, I know, Mister Boon. Right here in this suitcase is my academic hood." Mr. D. held it high for the old gent to see and pointed to the inner lining. "Cherry Red and White, Mr. Boon. The colours of *my* university – Temple University in Philadelphia."

"Quite nice, Suh. And Suh, supper won't be in the great 'all til term starts on Thursday. Rec'mend the pub food, though. The Bear Pub, right down the alley 'ere. where the Merton boys all go. Shepard's pie is mighty good. Suh."

"Well, my good man, after I get settled I was thinking about strolling the town and perhaps visiting some of the pubs."

"Well, Suh, you know we lock the portal doors at nine o'clock sharp."

"You mean there are "rules" even for the dons? Do I have to be in my quarters by nine o'clock every night?"

"No rules, Suh. Almost no regulations and such here, Suh. But the portal keeper locks the main doors, and if you're out, you're out for the night."

"Well, that's amazing. I can hardly believe it, Boon."

"Well, Suh, might as well start you 'right' from the first day, 'cause I'm your man. So 'ere's a key, my first boon to you, Suh."

Going to the window the old man pointed to the back of the compound. "The next courtyard, Suh, is the Fellows Garden. Way back in the far corner is a little oak door, and now you're holding the key that will unlock it and let you in any time that you please, Suh."

"Why, Boon, I already find you invaluable and indispensable!" Mr. D. held up the precious key with great delight. "My good man, this is wonderful!"

" You needn't tell anyone 'bout it, Suh. Had the keys to that door fifty years now. Wouldn't want the boys downstairs to find 'bout it, Suh. Master John."

"Boon, it is our very own secret. This little key is our bond of friendship. What can I ever do for you, dear man?"

"You're not supposed to anything for me, Suh. I'm your scout. Excuse me now, Suh. Need to give orders to the younger scouts. Some are only fifteen or sixteen like I was when I started 'ere in 1912."

Happiness and thrill were upon Mr. D. It was all joy and wonderment. He was at last at Oxford! His feet got wet going over the lawns to the "loo" in the back yards, the bed felt as if Oscar Wilde were still sleeping in it, and the great bells of Merton Tower almost knocked him out of bed as they ran every hour all through the night! But he truly loved it. Oxford was grand!

MOB QUAD: MERTON COLLEGE, OXFORD UNIVERSITY, OXFORD, ENGLAND

Mr. D's Set (apartment) was entered by the door, pictured center, and up stairs to the second floor. It had a living room and bedroom, but no loo.

Oscar Wilde (continued)

Merton College, Oxford University, Oxford, England.
From 1971-73 Mr. D. was a don and attained a doctorate at this renowned institution. His apartment was used by Oscar Wilde nearly one hundred years before. Wilde is still regarded as the most outstanding student ever to attend Oxford University, giving both the Solitarian and Valedictorian addresses at the graduation of his college class in 1878 at the Sheldonian Amphitheater. Untold books and plays have been written about his grand life, his conviction by English Courts, his two years in prison, and the very sad ending days of his life. He died in Paris, France, November 10, 1900 at the age of 46.

Oscar Wilde (continued)

STORY: "Matriculation Day" - Oxford University, Fall Term 1972

Sheldonian Amphitheater, Oxford University

The bells rang all about the University marking the opening of the fall term, called Matriculation Day. Mr. D. in full academic costume took his place with the dons of Merton College in the courtyard of the Sheldonian Amphitheater. The long academic procession of "fellows" and professors of the University was led by the Vice Chancellor, Harold MacMillan, a highly respected former Prime Minister of Great Britain. It was a great parade of academic regalia with gowns and hoods representing the great universities of the world. Many of the gowns were quite ornate with elaborate collars and strips of ermine. However, Oxford attire was strictly black and had been so since the days of the Puritans.

Following the Vice Chancellor was the University Provost carrying a huge, golden mace representing the royal authority of the Queen, who was the titular head of the institution. The great auditorium, built in the 1690's by Sir Christopher Wren, was a huge oval structure with many tiers of seats graduated up its interior walls. When the dons were all seated on the raised area behind the main podium, the year's Freshmen class, about 2500 boys and 500 girls, filed in to take their seats in the ground floor area.

According to the ancient Oxford University tradition, the welcome by the Provost, the prayer by the Chaplain, and even a few joking remarks were made in Latin. MacMillan was quite charming and certainly was the epitome of the British gentleman. "It is all quite wonderful," thought Mr. D.

Among the huge crowd in the courtyard after the ceremony was Warden Roberts, the headmaster of Merton College; his wife, Betty, and his overweight daughter, Pauline, who had a protruding jaw reminiscent of the Neanderthal Man. They were quick to to approach the new don from America.

"Well, what did you think, John?" said the Warden in a most cheery way.

"Most impressive! Absolutely tremendous!" exclaimed Mr.D.

" Yes. Now this is Betty, my dear wife, and Pauline, er, my daughter. I have asked them to show you the manner and ways of our university."

"So very nice to meet you, John. Pauline and I are looking forward to showing you everything here. You might even like to learn some of our sports," said Mrs. Roberts.

"Do you mean rugby and cricket, Mrs. Roberts?"

"Well, no. We couldn't teach those rough activities, but there is a splendid croquet court on our college lawns."

" And there is punting on the Cherwell River. You might like that,"said the daughter Pauline with awkward laughter.

"Well, Jack, you simply must come to tea at 4 o'clock on Saturday and meet all the fellows of Merton College. Our cottage is right within the college grounds," said the Warden's wife.

"And you should come to my study tomorrow at ten for a little chat about your lectures and such matters. Now, John, here's one of your scholars for the year. Oh, Birnley, over here, please. This is Mr. D. from America. He's to be your tutor this year. Perhaps you could show him around a bit this afternoon. John, this is Viscount Birnley, a junior at our college.

The young nobleman was a cousin of the Queen, and Mr.D. was taken aback to learn that he would be tutoring aristocracy!

"Yes, Sir, Warden Roberts," said Birnley. "The boys are going to meet at the Bear. I'll be quite glad to take our new tutor there and have him meet all of his new charges. Is that alright with you, Mr. D.? You know the Bear was a favorite pub of Oscar Wilde. It was built in the 1600's and it still stands there today.!

"Sound fine to me, Birnley. If Oscar Wilde liked it, I am sure that I will love that pub."

"Well, you chaps be off, and I shall be looking forward to our meeting in the morning, John," said the Warden departing with his wife and daughter.

The new don was much relieved to get away from that stuffy family and delighted to be with a student at last. "Do we alway have to wear these black gowns, Birnley?" inquired Mr. D.

"Well, to tell you the truth, Sir, it's a university tradition for all dons. We boys can wear almost anything, but they make us wear these short scholar's gowns so they can tell us apart from all the tourists."

"Oh, God, it feels like a huge kimono," lamented Mr. D.

"We can take a short cut through the grounds of Christ Church College. We'll be able to see the famous Tom Tower. And then down the alley for some tasty brews at the Bear, Sir."

"Yes, to the Bear, Birnley!" enjoined Mr. D., pointing himself in the direction of some much needed refreshment at Oscar Wilde's favorite drinking spot.

Punting on the Isis River, Oxford, England

Oscar Wilde (continued)

STORY: "The Tutorial Session" Oxford University, Fall Term 1972

Since the beginning of Oxford University in the 900's, the Tutorial Session every Friday was the custom. This meant the students, usually about 15, would meet with their tutors to go over what they had studied for the past week and to get some assignments.. Documents show that Oscar Wilde had the famous philosopher, John Ruskin, as his tutor, and legends indicate that there were often great verbal battles between the two scholars over points of philosophy.

Since Oxford operates on the tutorial system, Mr. D. was given fifteen young men as his charges that year. All were clever and bright and somewhat stylish in their manners. The only difference, alas, were their degrees of laziness. They seldom went to lectures, but when Mr.D. would inquire about attendance at important lectures, the standard answer was, "Much too busy, Sir!"

"Busy with what?" thought Mr. D. "Busy listening to records in their rooms all day?"

It was also a constant chore keeping track of the scholars. To be "in college" a student had to be within six miles of the Carfax Tower, a structure at the juncture of High Street and Haymarket in the center of the town. Most of the time he had no idea where his charges were; they were all masters of the polished excuse and the skillful evasion. Once he even heard that one of his boys had gone off to South Africa for a long weekend!

As often the practice at the university, dons held some of tutorial sessions in their own quarters, and Mr. D. thought it was a good idea to gather all fifteen of the boys in his apartment for group discussions. In the second week of St. Martin's Term, he planned to discuss the difference between the American and British societies and government, and he hoped every boy would show up.

"Why, Boon, everything looks very nice. Are you sure this will attract all my scholars?"

"Cream scones, various sandwiches, bangers, and lots of tea.. this will bring them in, Master John. You know that supper 'ere is not till eight or eight-thirty. The boys are as "ungry as "ounds" these afternoons. Like I tole you last week, a high tea always catches 'em"

"Well, I just cannot understand a political system where the Chief Executive, your President, is of one party and the legislature, and your Congress, is controlled by another party. I would suppose that very little would ever get done!" snorted Guy Weston, a cheeky student from Scotland.

"Well, sometimes I admit there is a stalemate. But Congress and the President are not always at odds," replied Mr. D.

"Well, this Nixon fellow certainly seems a bad egg. Will the Congress get rid of him?" asked Weston.

"Well, Weston, there is a provision in our Constitution for impeachment, but in 200 years a sitting President has never been removed from office."

"So, Sir, you don't think it will happen?" questioned Lors Cheswick.

"No. I just can't believe that it could happen. It would turn the entire American government on end.

"But we can get rid of a Prime Minister in a crack, Sir, and it doesn't upset the Kingdom at all." returned Cheswick. I certainly think, and perhaps you should too, conclude, that our system is better than yours."

"No, you have an upper chamber, the House of Lords, completely hereditary in membership or appointed by the Queen. That's anti-democratic, I must say," responded Mr. D. He had forgotten that one of the boys was the young Viscount of Birnley and he hoped he hadn't insulted the aristocracy.

Birnley was quick to break in. "Not being a totally disinterested person, I want to say that they could get rid of old Queen Lizzie and the whole royal log, for all I care. I am a Labor Socialist have no time for the Royal charade!"

After more discussion and the giving out of reading assignments, Mr. D. decided on a quick adjournment. "Well, my good gentlemen, enough for this afternoon. Next week ..and please be here next Friday.. we will discuss various American authors. Please do your readings, and be ready to contribute."

"Not to be indelicate, Sir, but will there be high teas?" asked Cheswick, whose huge hulk needed frequent feedings.

"Yes, yes, high tea, Cheswick. We will always present high tea. Isn't that right, Mr. Boon?" questioned Mr. D.

"Just as you say, Master John. Just as you say," responded the old butler.

Oscar Wilde (continued)

STORY: "Rag Week at Oxford" – Oxford University, Spring Term 1973

By the spring term, Mr. D. considered himself pretty much "anglicized" and "Oxfordized" in the manner of the great university and Oscar Wilde. He had learned to use English Colloquialisms and raise his voice a tone to emulate the great writer.

In his new vocabulary, refreshments were "savories" and sausages were "bangers". He had learned that "kippers" were little breakfast fish, "crisps" were potato chips, and "chips" were French Fries. In the course of the year, he had made a list of over a thousand English "English" words. His use of them was often enough to fool almost any Englishman into believing that he was "English". In the process of being "Oxfordized" he had learned how to play croquet, to punt on the rivers, to hold a cricket bat, and to eat with a fork held in his left hand.

The university year had Fall, Winter, and Spring Terms with long vacations in between. At the end of each term there was always great frivolity with parties, shows, (called cabarets), and contests. The most elaborate of these celebrations was Rag Week, at the end of Spring Term.

Among the most challenging of the contests was called the "Punt and Pint Race" up the Cherwell River. It was said that Oscar Wilde had visited Venice and bought the idea of small flat boats, called punts, pushed up the river by long poles. Wilde, a huge man, was known for the vast amount of beer that he could consume and, thus, he made up this contest. Each team, with the assistance of several "handlers" on the banks of the river, was to punt one hundred yards upstream, drink a British pint of ale, and then punt another hundred yards. The team which got the farthest up the river without passing out or falling out of the boat would be the winners.

Two of Mr. D.'s charges entered this contest. Sean Wentwell and Guy Weston both could consume vast amounts of ale and were the unanimous choices of their colleagues to represent Merton College.

"Aho, Mr D.! We're only 300 hundred yards up this blinking river, and I'm shitface already," yelled Guy Weston in drunken slobber.

"Com'on, Weston! Do it for old Merton!" shouted back the tutor with the utmost collegiate spirit.

"Too bad they don't have loos on these God-damned boats, Mr. D. I gotta piss bad, Sir!" yelled Sean Wentwell as he pushed on his pole with drunken laughter and relieved himself into the river.

When Sean and Guy fell out of their punt about one mile up the Cherwell, the hopes of Merton College for a victory were shattered .But it was great fun for all!

On Saturday of Rag Week the really big event, the "Three Legged Pub Crawl", took place, and that year the "honor" of Merton was at stake. For the past two years, the boys from St. John's College had bested them. Victory in 1973 was a must, and the task was put to young Viscount Birnley, who was nonpareil in debauchery, and Lors Cheswick, who when drinking the spirits was called "ape man".

For the third "man" on their team, the boys selected a buxom American student known for her reckless abandon. In this race, the member of the team in the middle had his legs bound with rags to the inner legs of the outer members. They were to gallop through the streets of Oxford and stop at 8 medieval pubs to drink a full pint of English beer!

About 60 teams were off at the starting gun around the rotary at the Radcliff Library. Then to the first stop, the King's Arms where "managers" had full pints foaming and ready. Judges were on hand to make sure that every drop was guzzled down!

Next stop was the Corn Dolly, a dingy pub behind the Cornmarket, and then to the Bulldog pub on Queen Street. Mr. D. greeted his college team at the Bear.

" Are you going to make it, Birnley?" shouted Mr.D, who was by this time pretty drunk himself.

" You bet your ass, Sir, but this American bird weighs a bloody ton," laughed Birnley.

"Hey, Mr. D. Are all American broads as dignified as this one. She says she's gotta pee," yelled Cheswick.

"Do whatever needs to be done, Cheswick, old boy," hollered Mr. D.

Tied together, the two boys and the girl stumbled into the Bear to get the girl bladder relief. Somehow, without being untied the young lady got her urine emptied.

After visiting several more pubs, the Merton team squeezed its way down the narrow passage to the last pub, the Chequers. Cheswick, with brute strength, dragged his two compatriots to the door of the ancient saloon. Victory was theirs.. and Merton's. This called for a virtual deluge of drinking by all members of the Merton community.

Rag Week culminated at 6 o'clock on Sunday with a salute to the dawn called "May Morning". And what a scene to behold! On the Isis River, hundreds of Oxford boys, wearing straw skimmers and blue blazers, were sitting in the punts with their pretty sweethearts, all dressed up in flouncy white dresses. Up above on the roof of the great bell tower of Magdalene College sang a choir of university men and boy sopranos. As the great tower bells rang out, they sang their tribute to "May Morning."

"This was Oxford at its grandest – tradition, culture, beauty, and romance," thought Mr. D. Just as he dreamed it would be. As he stood on the Magdalene Bridge beholding the whole wonderful spectacle and looking up at the great bell tower, He could finally say to himself with pride and pleasure, "It is so wonderful to be an Oxford don!"

"May Morning" Celebration during "Rag Week" at the end of the Spring Term. The Oxford Choir sings standing on the top of the Madgalene Tower and students and their girl friends are in the punts along the Cherwell River. As the Sun comes up, they sing a welcoming to spring, an ages- old tradition at Oxford University.

CELEBRITY 14: 1972: J. R. R. Tolkien
(1892 – 1973)

1925: Student at Oxford U.   1972: Professor Emeritus
Merton College

STORY: "The Very Manner of Things"

Eating was fine social activity at Merton College, at Oxford University, and the meals seemed to go on all day. Hours of meals were posted by the huge oaken doors of the great dining hall: when opened, food was to be served.

Breakfast was at one's leisure, just as long as one got there before the dining hall doors closed promptly at eight o'clock. Morning repast was similar to American fare except for the fried tomatoes, baked beans, kippers, and bangers. Promptly at eleven o'clock "morning coffee" was presented in buffet style at the end of the dining room, along with some cakes and sandwiches (for those who couldn't wait for lunch).

Service by the scouts was on majestic pewter plates. Elegant silver cups and silverware emblazoned with the college's coat of arms were bought out for every meal. It was said that the scouts had sworn with their lives to preserve and protect these precious Merton heirlooms.

The interior of Merton College's great dining hall was awesome and dignified. The atmosphere was that of a medieval castle. All about the walls hung large painted portraits of famous alumni: aristocracy, admirals, bishops, professors. At the formal dinner on Thursday nights, there would be a ringing of the giant Merton bells, and the dons would come in and take their places on the raised dais, followed by the scholars, who sat at long high wooden tables with their feet on low wooden benches (replacements for foot warmers of earlier periods). The cuisine was always quite fine, and food was rushed in on huge silver platters from the steam tables in the hallway. Supper at eight was always a ceremonial affair, beginning with grace in Latin. On Thursdays, prominent guests were usually invited.

While the boys were finishing their desserts of lemon pudding, Professor Roberts, the Warden of the College, would rise to make his announcements. Usually his dignified pronouncements centered on poor attendance at chapel, or the problem of rowdy behavior, but on one Thursday night, the pronouncement concerned a most eminent guest.

"We are most honored again to have with us here in hall tonight, gentlemen and scholars, a most distinguished member of our staff, the famous novelist, Professor J.R.R. Tolkien." The four hundred assembled boys eating their dessert paused long enough to give some polite applause. "Professor Tolkien will soon celebrate his eighty-third year as a subject of our beloved monarchy. He declines making any remarks this evening, but he extends to all here his greatest regards and expresses his love and loyalty to our Merton College."

After dinner, Mr. D. went into the Fellow Lounge which offered some coffee, brandy, and cigarettes. Service was by some young, fumbling scouts; and Professor Tolkien sat by the fireplace sipping some brandy. The other dons soon went on their way, and the American don was left alone with the greatest author of recent British fiction! What would he say? What could he say to this great celebrity?

Mr. D. fumbled in front of the fireplace. He wanted to say something brilliant, perhaps about the great works of the author. What inspired "The Lord of the Rings"? Where did the name "Hobbit" come from? It all sounded so unsophisticated so he just announced, "I'm from America, Professor," hoping to get a response.

"Yes, Yes, from the colonies," he said sucking on his pipe.

"From New Jersey. Actually from the Philadelphia area."

"Yes, Yes, I've heard of those places."

"Terrible weather we're having, Professor."

"Yes, young man, quite dreadful."

Mr. D.'s face burned with redness, and he did not know if it was caused by the heat of the flames or his embarrassment at not being able to start a conversation. Mercifully, Warden Roberts arrived and spoke to the flustered American, calling him aside. "Well, John, my daughter and wife are finding you absolutely delightful as a pupil of our University ways."

"Well, Sir, Pauline and Mrs. Roberts have been very generous with their time teaching me croquet. I don't think I will ever get the hang of it."

Well, Man, come better weather. You just stick with it. We all learn the Oxford ways sooner of later.

Mr. D. often encountered J.R.R. Tolkien, the great writer; it was always in the Fellows Lounge after a great dinner at Merton College. One evening Mr. D. decided to be bold and ask a question about the author's great works.

"Professor Tolkien, I always wondered why the good tribes were always losing to the Great Evil, except when all the tribes, including the Dead, all came together and defeated the Great Evil. Why was it written that way, sir?"

"'The Lord of the Rings' was mostly an allegory, with the Great Evil representing Hitler and the Nazi. For a while, during the great air raids and the destruction, I almost thought that we would lose the war and the Germans would take over of country."

On other occasions when they would meet, they usually discussed the bad English weather, drank some brandy, and just enjoyed being Oxford dons. The professor, at his age, was rather forgetful and Mr. D. would often have to reintroduce himself. .

"Oh, yes, you're the chap from the colonies," the great writer would say, as he puffed pensively on his pipe and took another sip of Brandy.

J. R. R. Tolkien (continued)

Poster for "The Lord of the Rings"   Poster for "The Hobbit"

Mr. D. often associated with J. R.R. Tolkien when he was a don and the author was a Professor Emeritus at Merton College, Oxford University. The author's two most famous books have been published throughout the world and made into popular motion pictures. His other well-known books are, "The Silmarillion", unfinished but completed by Tolkien's son, and the "Twin Towers". He was a scholar of Nordic history, and all of his books are based on tales from Scandinavia.

J. R. R. Tolkien (continued)

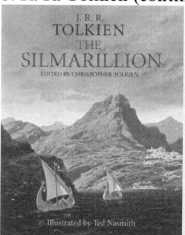 

Book cover: "The Silmarillion" Poster for "The Two Towers"

Martin Freeman (left) & Dwarfs in scene from "The Hobbit" movie

CELEBRITY 15: 1973: Debbie Reynolds
(1936 – present)

1962: "Singing in the Rain"   1987:"Sadie & Son" TV Movie
Movie

STORY: "Mr. D. Meets Actress Debbie Reynolds"

As Mr. D. was sauntered down Broad Street, a main street in Philadelphia, he saw the huge marquee of the Schubert Theater. He thought he would stop in and see his pal and former student, Tad Dynakowski, who was the assistant manager.

"Hello, John, what are you doing here?" questioned Tad.

"I was just passing by so I decided to stop in and see what was going on in here."

"Well, up on the stage you can see they're getting ready for a production. It's the musical "Irene", an old play written in the 1920's. The producers have bought in Debbie Reynolds to do the lead, and this old Shakespearean actor, Sir John Gielgud, to direct. He wants to be called "Suh Jin.""

"Well, I can understand Debbie Reynolds, she's a big Hollywood star, but why this old British guy as director."

"Oh, they thought it would help sell the play when it got to Broadway. Besides no other director wanted to do it. That's Debbie Reynolds up there."

There were all sorts of hammering and noises as the carpenters were working on the sets, and there was an annoying whining sound coming from the adjustments to the sound system.

"Here comes Debbie up the aisle now," said Tad

She was wearing a smock and her hair was all in a mess.

"Tad, did any mail come for me here at the theatre? My Agent, Sid Balstein, said the contracts for the Broadway run would be sent here."

"I checked this morning. I didn't see any mail for you."

"Doing this ancient play is bad enough, without having this half- dead director. He may know a lot about Shakespeare, but he doesn't know anything about Broadway shows. And the lines in this play are so trite; they make me gag just saying them. Where is that old fag? "

"He went downstairs to the bathroom," said Mr. D.

"And who are you?" asked Debbie

"This is my old high school teacher, John D'Alessandro"

"Well, John, or whatever your name is. Do me a favor. Will you please go down there and tell his highness to pull up his knickers and get the hell up here. I'm ready to go."

Mr. D. went out to the lobby and down the stairs to the smoking lounge. There he found the old Englishman pacing about.

"Mr. Gielgud, Miss Reynolds sent me to tell you she is ready to proceed."

"Well, that old Trollope can just wait until I have a few more ciggees."

After pacing about and smoking some more he continued, "You seem like a friendly young man. Can you tell me if there any risqué clubs around here?"

"Well, right across Broad Street is Locust St.; they call it the Gayborhood."

"That's great. How about you and I go for a drink.. you know just a short one, and all that?"

Mr. D. felt uncomfortable and realized the old guy was "hitting" on him.

Pulling out a wad of American dollars, he waved them and said, "They gave me all this money to come here to Philadelphia. Would it be indelicate to offer you some of these bills. You could join me at my hotel."

"That's a kind invitation, Suh Jin. But I'm a school teacher, and I have to be at my high school by 8:00 tomorrow morning."

"Teachers.. Ach! They're so depressing. Well, go up and tell the Prima Donna I'll be there shortly."

Back in theater, he reported to the lead lady, "Suh Jin, said he would be here presently.

"Well, you can help with another problem, Carrie, my daughter. Carrie Fisher. You know that I was once married to Eddie Fisher and now I have his kids. I don't know where she is."

"Where do you think she should be?" asked Mr. D.

"She should be in our room at the Bellevue Stratford Hotel, a block away. But yesterday, she was running around with Ed Bacon's sons, Kevin and Bob Bacon. I think they were playing guitars and singing on Rittenhouse Square. They want to form a group called, "The Bacon Boys" and want Carrie to join them as a singer. But no way. She's coming with me to New York when we start the Broadway run with this play in 6 weeks. Look, John, here's the key to my hotel room, number 307. Please go there and see if she's there. She might be sleeping. If not go out a find her, someplace, any place. I'll pay you anything. Will you do that? I'm really worried about her. Here's my phone number, and here's her picture! She's wearing a New York Yankees baseball cap and jacket."

Somehow Mr. D. had gotten drawn into the troubles of the famous movie star. How was he to find the lost daughter?.

"Tad, Debbie wants me to go looking for Carrie Fisher, so I'm leaving."

"O.K., give me call next week; I'll give you tickets to this show when it opens."

Dutifully, Mr.D. went to the Bellevue Stratford Hotel, and to Room 307. The room was empty. Where would a teenager go? First to Rittenhouse Square; then to the Reading Terminal Food Market, then just frantically searching up and down the main streets, looking for a teenager wearing a New York Yankees baseball cap and jacket.

Exhausted and feeling defeated, he thought he would go again to Debbie's room at the Bellevue Stratford Hotel. After entering, he saw the outline of a young female body in the bed. He picked up the phone and dialed, "Hello, Debbie... Debbie Reynolds.. Yes I found her. She's here asleep in bed."

He could hear the actress's sigh of relief and hear her say, "Thank you, John. Thank Goodness, my daughter's O.K. Anyway for now."

Debbie Reynolds (continued)

1973: Mr. D. met Debbie Reynolds during a 6 weeks run of the musical "Irene" in Philadelphia. The play went to Broadway and she was nominated for the Tony Award as Best Lead Actress in a Musical. The photo above shows the actress & cast in the Finale.

Debbie Reynolds is an American actress, singer, entertainer, business woman, and film historian. In 1964, she starred in "The Unsinkable Molly Brown" and was nominated for an Academy Award. Other notable films include "The Singing Nun" (1966) "Divorce American Style (1967) "What's the Matter with Helen" (1971) and "In and Out" (1997). She won the Golden Globe Award for "Mother" in 1997. Among her three husbands, was Eddie Fisher, a well known singer. Her daughter, Carrie Fisher, is now a famous Hollywood screenplay writer.

CELEBRITY 16: 1976: Queen Elizabeth
(1926 – present)

1953: Crowned as Queen of U.K   1976: Phila.: U. S. Bicentennial

STORY: "Mr. D. and the Queen of Great Britain"

Gong, Gong, Gong, Gong rang the bell in the tower of Independence Hall in Philadelphia. Mr. D., often a guide at Independence National Park, knew that the bell was the Centennial Bell, sent to the United States by Queen Victoria in 1876. The famous Liberty Bell, now in its own pavilion on the mall, became cracked when rung upon the death of Supreme Court Justice Marshall in 1835. Now in July of 1976 a 3rd bell, the Bicentennial Bell, to celebrate the country's 200th birthday, was to be bought from England by Her Majesty, Queen Elizabeth. She would arrive on the Royal Yacht, the Britannia, on July 1st and would present the bell to the City of Philadelphia on July 6h. All three of the bells were made at the same Whitechapel Bell

Foundry in London. At a riverside park, know as Penn's Landing, Mr. D. was right behind the guide ropes on the gang plank, as the Royal Personage debarked from the great ship. While slowly stepping over the rough boards, she tripped and was almost tumbling when reached out over the ropes and grabbed the teacher by the sleeve and tugged on it trying to steady herself. Her aides were aghast. The Queen of the British Empire had actually touched a "commoner" and a "nobody".

With majestic demeanor she became completely calm and walked with her equerries to the National Park Visitor's Center on Third Street. There she was to make a speech and ring the Bicentennial Bell, which had been installed in the building's tower the earlier..

After many speeches by the Mayor of Philadelphia and various other officials, the Queen approached the podium. She was to make her remarks and then push the button to ring the Bicentennial Bell for the very first time.

"I speak to you as the direct descendent of King George III.." The bell in the tower started to ring loudly but suddenly stopped. Not frustrated the monarch continued. "I speak to you as the direct descendant of King George III " .. The bells started once again to ring and ring loudly and then suddenly stopped. "I speak to you as the direct descendant King George III..." . The Queen had had enough, "Oh, hell with it!" she said in dismay. Her speech was never given, but it was emblazoned on a bronze plaque that was placed on a two foot pylon before the building and remained there for over 50 years until the old Independence Park Visitors' Center was torn down

The Queen in all her glory walked with her entourage back to the royal yacht. On board, she held court meeting various state and federal officials. Mr. D. trailed her on her return walk. He really wanted to run up the gangplank and get aboard the boat, but there were too many guards and policeman. At any rate he had been "touched" by the great Queen. It was a touch of wonder and magic, and he savored the incident for a very long time.

Royal Yacht "Britannia" brought the Queen to Philadelphia in 1976

Queen Elizabeth (continued)

Princess Elizabeth married Philip Mountbatten in 1947. Upon the death of her father George VI, she became Monarch of the British Empire in 1953. As of 2016, at the age of ninety, she had been Queen for 63 years. Mr. D. had a brief encounter with Her Majesty during the Bicentennial when she left the Royal Yacht, Brittania.

Queen & grandson Prince William, third in line for the Throne

CELEBRITY 17: 1977: Woody Allen
(1935 – present)

1960's: Stand-up Comedian Hall"

1977: Academy Award for "Annie

STORY: "Mr. D. Meets Woody Allen"

"It's Woody Allen himself. The writer of this play that we are seeing tonight, right over there" said Mr. D. "It's opening night. This is the first presentation of his play. Naturally the playwright would be here. This is the first performance of 'Don't Drink the Water'. "Are you students enjoying it?"

"Well, I don't understand it much. But it seems pretty funny. So he's the little, skinny guy with fuzzy hair, pacing back and forth. Let's go over and talk to him," said Bob Miller, a 10th grade student.

Mr. D. gathered his group of four drama students. They went out of the Walnut Street Theatre and approached a very nervous playwright.

"The audience hates it! I know they hate it! Everybody is going to walk out of the theatre during the second act. Already I saw the newspaper critics leave. I know they are going to kill this show!" Woody Allen was talking out loud to himself and was his usual nervous wreck.

"Mr. Allen.. may we.., " started Mr. D.

"Who's Mr. Allen. Mr. Allen is my father. I'm Woody. Don't tell me that you guys already hate my play. I'm already dying."

"No, No, Woody.. we really enjoyed the first act.. it's pretty good," commented Bob Miller

"Pretty good.. not even good? Well, kid, what about you.. is it terrible?"

"No, Woody.. really, it's pretty good," said Harry Konak in all sincerity.

"Pretty.. enough already with the 'pretty.' "

"Well, it's a bundle of laughs, hah, hah, hah," came back Bob.

"What are you a comedian? Everybody wants to be a comedian. How am I going to make a living if everybody wants to be a comedian? Well, you guys get in there for the Second Act... it really comes alive... I promise yea, yea, really alive and all that... you'll like it.. eh.. maybe. And please applause a lot!"

"If this play is O.K. could we give it at our high school.. it's Collingwood High School in Collingswood, New Jersey."

"New Jersey.. yea,.. that's where my plays end up... in New Jersey... Listen I'm sure the producer is going to close down this play tonight. If you kids ever get to give this play in New Jersey, it will be only the second performance!. Don't you kids get it? I knew this was a bad idea. A Catholic cardinal hiding in the American Embassy in Budapest. What do I know about Budapest.. or even about Catholic cardinals.. oyvay.. I'm such a smuck when it comes to ideas for plays. I can even see the headlines for the review tomorrow, "Woody Allen Play at Walnut Theater Bombs!'

Mr. D. and his four students went in the theater for the second act, and at the final curtain there was polite applause, except for his gang who clapped heartily. The audience quickly exited into the night's summer air, leaving the distressed playwright pacing back and forth in the lobby.

He approached the departing group. "Well, kidos, it was a disaster wasn't it? Wasn't it?"

"No. No. We liked it. We liked it. I applauded so much my hands began to hurt," said young Bob Miller.

"Didn't you hear me, shouting Bravo! Bravo?" added Mr. D.

"Look I got to get back on the train to New York. Do you guys ever get up to the big city? You know I sit in at Eddie Condon's Jazz Club every Thursday night. You should come."

"Why do you play in a band, if you're writing plays, Mr. Allen.. I mean Woody?" asked Harry Konak.

"Listen, smarty, with me writing zonky plays like this.. I'm going to end up on the street with a tin cup. Playing sax is my only back-up.".

Mr. D. and his four students did enjoy, "Don't Drink the Water", but even they didn't think it would be a hit. After the show, they took the bus back to Collingswood with the memory that they had met the fidgety comedy writer, who eventually became the great film maker, Woody Allen.

Despite the playwright's misgivings, the play was a success and played on Broadway for a couple of years. Subsequently, it was probably presented by every high school and little theatre in America.

Whenever Mr. D. went to New York City, he was sure to stop in to Eddie Condon's Jazz Club on Thursday nights to see Woody Allen play the sax and chat with him.

" Woody, that was great music tonight. I'm really getting to like jazz."

" Oh you're the school teacher , who doesn't like my plays," said Woody trying to "put on" Mr. D.

" Woody, I directed 'Don't Drink the Water" this year, at my high school in New Jersey."

"Yes, in Jersey. That doesn't count! That where all my plays end up!" said Woody trying to razz the teacher.

A few years later, Mr. D. decided to present and direct "Play It Again, Sam" In retrospect, he well remembered that very first performance of "Don't Drink the Water" at the Walnut Street Theatre in Philadelphia. And how Woody Allen was such a nervous wreck, and how Woody himself thought the play would be a failure. But it proved to be one of his most popular plays. Woody Allen went on to write a few more plays but many, many screenplays for his over 40 movies.

Woody Allen (continued)

1966-68: Woody Allen directed the cast of his own play "Don't Drink the Water" at various Broadway Theaters. The play was about a group of unusual characters, who because of the Communist regime had taken refuge in the American embassy in Budapest. The cast included Anthony Roberts in the lead role, along with Kay Medford, Amita Gillette, Luke Andreas, Jonathan Bolt, Oliver Clark, James Dukas, John Hallow, House Jameson, Dick Lambertini, Gerry Matthews, Donna Mills , Sharon Talbot, Gene Varrone, and Curtis Wheeler. After the Broadway, run it was subsequently made into a mildly successful Hollywood movie.

Woody Allen (continued)

Poster: "Don't Drink the Water" play a film   Poster: "Play It Again, Sam" the play as a film

Woody Allen is an American actor, comedian, filmmaker, playwright, and musician whose career spans more than six decades. In the 1950's he was a comedy writer for various comedians and comedy shows. In the 1960s he worked as stand-up comedian. By the mid-60's, Allen was writing and directing films, first specializing in slapstick comedies before moving into dramatic material. He often performs in his own films. He has written and produced over thirteen play and forty movies, winning Academy Awards three times. He presents a new film every year.
Mr. D. met Woody Allen at the opening of "Don't Drink the Water" at the Walnut Theatre in Philadelphia in 1977 and afterwards they became friends. They often see each other at Eddie Condon's Jazz Club on 57th Street in New York City.

CELEBRITY 18: 1978: Frank Rizzo
(1920 – 1991)

1940's: Phila. Police Dept.   1967-71: Phila. Police Commissioner

STORY: "Mr. D. Meets Mayor Frank Rizzo"

"Frank's, is one of the best, if not the best Italian restaurant in South Philly," declared one of Mr. D.'s best friends, Tad Dynakowski, trying to park his car on the very congested 9th Street.

"What is that mob in front of the restaurant? Maybe we should go somewhere else"

"Not on your life; I'm really hungry and we are going to eat here," said Tad.

There were about 25 blacks carrying signs that said, "No Center City Tunnel!" "No Market East Station" "500 Million for A Train Tunnel", "Stop Mayor Rizzo Now!"

Tad was a huge 6 foot five person and he led Mr. D. into the crowd. They were harassed and hassled about by the protestors, but the two finally got to the door where two bouncers let them into the restaurant. The eating place was jammed with mid-day diners, but in the middle at a special table, sat Frank Rizzo, the Mayor of Philadelphia, with Ed Bacon, Philadelphia's City Planner, and a huge black bodyguard with all his guns showing.

The Mayor called them over to his table. "Do youse guys know what a conservative is? ... He's a liberal who got mugged the night before!" he said with a great laugh. "Did those niggers rough you up?"

"They torn my shirt and ripped the sleeve on my coat. They wrestled with my friend here; they were trying to prevent us from coming in here."

"Those damn jungle bunnies. I should have them all arrested, but I don't want to cause a big incident right now. If there are any reporters listening.. I meant "Afroid-Americans!"
. Then he stood up. " Yoh!," he yelled, "are there any reporters here? Come over here!"

A short of wimpy person appeared, "I sometimes write for the Philadelphia Weekly, What do you want?"

"I want you to report in your paper that these agistators from the "Move Black Squad" assaulted two patrons at Ralph's restaurant. What are your names, guys?"

"I'm John D'Alessandro, a teacher from Collingswood, New Jersey"

"And I'm Tad Dynakowski, I'm Assistant Manger at the Shubert Theater"

"Youse guys sit right here, next to my table, so we can talk. Those black thugs are protesting because they don't want the city to build an underground station, to be called Market East; it will be right under the Gallery Mall with 300 stores. This is my friend, Ed Bacon. He's the city planner, and it's all his idea. And I think it a great idea. It will give Philly a world-wide reputation-up for innovation"

"Well. Mr. Mayor, I've seen extensive plans in the newspapers. It will mean all the regional trains, including those from New Jersey and , Delaware, will be able to come right into center city. And people will do their shopping right there at the Gallery Mall. I think it's great!"

"Mister, we should hire you as our P.R. man. You got the idea right!" But what about the 500 million that it will cost? The "Move" people think that money should be spent on black causes."

"Spend that money on black causes and it will all quickly disappear! A fantastic, beautiful, underground train station would last maybe for a hundred years," said Mr. D.'s friend, Tad

"Well, it's gonna be thisa way guys. I'm the mayor and Ed Bacon here is the city planner, and a whole jungle of black guys are not gonna stop the ground-breaking ceremony for the tunnel next Saturday! I assure you if there is any interfere from these thugs, a lot of black heads are gonna get hit by police clubs. We're gonna have the tunnel, no matter who's against it!! Because I say so! God damn it!!"

"Well, we better order our lunch. Here is the waiter. I going to have the lasagna and meatballs."

"Well, nice meeting youse guys. Ed and I gotta get out of here. We've got a lot to do for the tunnel. And by the way, your lunch check is on me."

After the episode Mr. D. thought the Mayor Rizzo was a pretty nice guy, and maybe all that bad publicity about his being a dictator was wrong. Mr. D. knew then that the Market East Underground Train Station would be built, because Frank Rizzo demanded it. He also thought that he wanted to be on the first train to go into the tunnel.

Frank Rizzo (continued)

**1945: Phila. Motorcycle Cop   Rizzo statue stands before
City Services Bldg. It was paid for by public subscription**

Frank Rizzo joined the Philadelphia Police Department in 1940, rising through the ranks to serve as a tough, hands-on police commissioner from 1967 to 1971. He raided the offices of the Black Panthers in August of 1970. He once was reported to say, "Once I get finished with them, I'll make Attila the Hun look like a fag."   He was elected to his first term of as Mayor of the city in 1972 and reelected in 1976. He often held press conferences in which he discussed matters in colorful and bombastic manner.

His brother, Joseph Rizzo, was the Fire Commissioner, and because of complaints of racial discrimination by the two Rizzos, the "Philadelphia Plan" was adopted to assure affirmative action in civil service hiring. During his tenure Rizzo was credited with the completion the Center City Commuter Connection, later called the Market East Station, which permitted all regional rail lines to come into center city by underground tunnel.

CELEBRITY 19:   1996: Donald Trump
(1946 – present)

1960: at Wharton School   **2016: Presidential Run**

STORY: "Mr. D. Meets Donald Trump"

Mr. D. sat by the large windows overlooking the Delaware River and waited for his friend, Dick Scudder, to arrive for lunch. The George the Second Inn, dated from 1666, was a stately eating place with completely Colonial Décor. As the teacher kept noting the lateness of his pal, he saw across the aisle a dapper man, with orange hair and an orange tie, tapping his fingers impatiently on the white table cloth. Unexpectedly, the man signaled with cupped hand for Mr. D to join him.

"What's your name, sir?" asked the man with the orange hair.

"John D'Alessandro"

"That's Italian or something?

"Yes, my father was born in Italy My mother was born in Philadelphia."

"I'm Donald Trump, you can call me Don. I've been waiting for the last hour for three ginzoes from the Bristol Town Commission to get here."

"Yes, I recognize you, Don. I am waiting myself for my friend to arrive for lunch and I'm starving!"

"You might think these whops, would have some consideration. I'm here to offer them a great deal. I want their O.K. to put a beautiful casino ship right here at the dock of Bristol, Pennsylvania, right here on the river."

"Do you think they'll go for it, Don?"

"They'll go for it alright. See it's all in the deal... the art of the deal..you maneuver the terms until they can't say 'no' "

"Well, first I'll tell them how beautiful the boat is and all that. Then I tell them we'll fix up roads, give money to the schools, and all that."

"And if that doesn't work?"

"Then there are personal benefits. You know in New York City we call it "vigorish".. the little payoff. Without the "vig" nothing happens in the Big Apple.. with 'vig' you get the building super to fix your bathroom, with "vig" the cop makes a parking place for you, with "vig" the doorman forgets what he saw.. So if I give a little "vig" to these grease balls, they'll come around."

"Well, excuse me, Don, but that sounds close to bribery."

"No way. I'll offer each of them a $20,000 comp at my Trump Plaza Casino on the Boardwalk in Atlantic City. That's perfectly legal. Done all the time. John, you better get back to your table here they come..."

Just then three ominous looking men all dressed in black came into the restaurant. Mr. D. overheard them introducing themselves, but he couldn't hear all the heated discussion that went on between the men and Trump."

Dick Scudder finally arrived and they ordered some cocktails and fish dinners. Dick was a member of the "Sons of the American Revolution" with a family history going back before the 1700's. Today he was telling Mr. D. about the colonial Scudder Plantation and how the Scudder Falls Bridge, crossing the Delaware River, was named after his ancestors. Mr. D. was quite intrigued by the great and long story.

Suddenly the three Councilmen from Bristol, Pennsylvania, trudged down the aisle and out of the restaurant. In a few minutes Donald Trump approached Mr. D. and his friend at their table.

"God Damn It! Those lousy whops didn't take the deal! I offered them $60,000 in Trump Casino comps. It was an offer they couldn't refuse, but they did. I really hate to say it but I think they're HONEST!"

Mr. D. couldn't stop himself from laughing at the very annoyed big time executive, flustered because he couldn't, for once, make a "deal"

"D'Alessandro, I find Italians are the dumbest people in the world, I spent good time with these ignorant jackasses. These foreigners should all be deported back to Italy!" said Trump as he quickly exited the restaurant.

Mr. D. and Dick Scudder laughed a bit and then they raised their cocktail glasses and toasted all Italians throughout the world.

With bluster and bragging about of the crazy things that he would do, Trump won 16 State Primaries and the GOP candidacy for the President of the U.S.

Donald Trump (continued)

The Trump Tower, at Fifth Avenue and 56th Street is the headquarters of the Trump Organisation and home of its owner, Donald Trump. Three Trump Corporation casinos, including the Trump Taj Mahal in Atlantic City NJ, have all fallen into bankruptcy and sold at great loss to their investors. During his campaign, he repeatedly said he made a great deal of money on the casinos deals. In the resort he was known for not paying construction bills, and then settling for half or less, cheating contractions and other suppliers.

CELEBRITY 20: 1996: Bill Gates
(1955 – present)

1977: Student at Harvard   **Forbes Magazine: "Richest Man in the World."**

Boom, crash, roar, rattle, buzz, drum rolls, trumpet blasts, cymbals crashing, thumping on the bass violin, beating on the tympanis, ringing of the chimes, weird sounds from the tubas, wails of the clarinets, and all sorts of discondant noises. This was the music for "The New Symphony for the Computer" played the renowned Philadelphia Orchestra at the cavernous Academy of Music hall in Philadelphia, Pennsylvania, on November 12, 1996. This weirdest of compositions was commissioned to celebrate the 50th Anniversary of the invention of the ENIAC, the first electronic computer, at the Moore School of Electrical Engineering by doctoral students John W. Mauchly and J. Presper Eckert Jr. during the early 40's.

In the first row of the opera house were several dignitaries and the persons to be honored that night. Unfortunately the two inventors of the ENIAC had passed away, but in their stead their widows, Mary Walzl Mauchly and Ann Eckert, along early computer programmer, Jean Jennings Bartick was to receive the awards. Mr.D. had been asked by Jean Bartick to be her escort for the concert. Also sitting in the same row were guests of the evening, Bill Gates, president of the Microsoft Corporation, and his wife, Melinda

The concert being played was so discordant audience members could speak right out and not disturb the "Music". "Did you ever hear such ear-shattering noises? And they said they paid that crazy Czeck composer $50,000 for all this musical insanity," complained Jean Bartick

"Well, he was told to make it sound like the giant ENIAC computer with all the reels spinning about and the radio tubes blowing out. But I agree. It's really terrible."

The large audience suffered though the musical travesty. It was later said that the symphony was never played again!

In the lobby of the opera house, Melinda Gates gathered with Mary Mauchly, Ann Eckert, and Jean Bartick to tell them about her four children. While the women's talk was going on, Mr. D. was left to talk to Bill Gates.

"Wow! That was horrendous! I was wishing I had ear plugs!" said Gates.

" Mr. Gates, Bill, did you ever meet the two inventors?" questioned Mr. D. starting a conversation

"Yes, I knew them both. John Mauchly died in 1980 and Presper Eckert died just last year. Their work was revolutionary; because of them we got rid of the old IBM system of punch cards and reels of tapes. Their machine was 1000 times faster than any calculating device in existence… It seems the whole faculty of Penn Electrical Engineering is here tonight. Where did you go to school?"

. "Well, the local Temple University for two degrees and then to Oxford for a doctorate."

"Well, I guess the whole country knows I left Harvard in my third year."

" Bill, did you ever think about finishing?"

"Oh, hundreds of colleges have wanted to give me a honorary doctorate, but what they really want is for me to speak at their commencements. And I seldom do that."

"Well, I hear that your Gates Foundation supports many good causes, especially in Africa. But what about our cities? What we need in Philadelphia and for poor schools around the country are computer rooms for disadvantaged kids. "

"Well, we have put thousands of computers in public libraries all around the country. But poor schools? How could we identify them?"

"Any school where over half of the students qualify for the Federal Lunch Program is a poor school."

"Yea, that's right. That sounds like a good idea. Would you mind if I took that proposal to the directors of the Gates Foundation? Of course, my wife, Melinda, is the president. I think she might go for the idea."

After the concert, all of the invited audience walked over to the Bellevue Stratford Hotel a block away, for the big anniversary dinner. After the dessert and coffee were served the speeches of the night began. On behalf of their deceased husbands, Mary Mauchly and Ann Prosper, were honored with posthomonous membership In the National Academy of Engineering. Jean Bartik, as leader of the six original women programmers of the ENIAC, was given the Computer Pioneer Award for her work in creating the master program for the giant computer.

At the long banquet table where they sat, Mr. D. did get to chat with Bill and Melinda Gates, and they became quite friendly. The person declared by Forbes Magazine as "Richest Man on Earth" was very quiet and humble. When he was called upon to make some remarks, he silently waved "decline."

As the banquet was breaking up, the Gates couple approached Mr. D. and his date, Jean Bartick. "Jean and John, Bill and I would be very happy to have you visit our home in Seattle. I guess it is quite special," said Melinda Gates

"That's a very nice invitation," said Mr. D.

Jean Bartick spoke up. "Now, Bill is it true that the light panels in the rooms in your Seattle house change according to the body temperature of the person that enters."

"Yes" answered Bill, "it's pretty nifty. But the house is often cold. You know Seattle weather."

"Well, can't you devise a computer program to fix that?" asked Mr. D.

"John, we're working on that. I can assure you that we'll have it fixed by the time you and Jean visit us."

For John D'Alessandro and Jean Bartick, his date, it had been an wonderful evening. The inventors and early programmers of the ENIAC would not be forgotten for a long time by all who were there for the 50th Anniversay Celebration.

Bill Gates (continued)

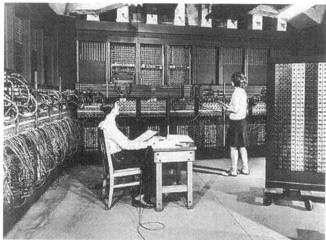

ENIAC calculator is now on display at School of Electrical Engineering, University of Pennsylvania.
This monstrous calculator, was developed during the early 1940s, and was used to compute ballistics for World War II. It was operated by six female programmers, led by Jean Jennings Bartick, a computer pioneer, and good friend of Mr. D.

Bill Gates (continued)

Bill Gates' $123 million Mansion outside Seattle, Washington

Upon a previous invitation to visit, John D'Alessandro and date, Jean Bartick, a pioneer developer of the ENIAC, visited the fantastic home of Bill and Melinda Gates in April,, 1997. It was an appropriate residence for the richest man in the U.S. and his charming wife. John and Jean greatly enjoyed roaming the 66,000 square feet home with 65 rooms and 24 bathrooms. They found that it had a high-tech sensor that automatically adjusted the lighting and temperature of the rooms to a guest's body temperature. The artwork could be changed at the touch of a button and the pool had an underwater music system .There was a garage that can accommodate 23 cars . John and Jean were wonderfully entertained by Bill and Melinda Gates.

BUY COPIES OF THIS BOOK ONLINE WITH YOUR COMPUTER

Purchase additional copies of "Celebrities! Celebrities! Mr.D.'s Amazing Encounters with Famous People" and pay for it on Amazon.com @ $14.95 each. Order by author's name or the title of this book.

A book autographed by the author will be sent to your address promptly by U.S. Mail.